MORE PRAISE FOR *MODERN FOODS*

The powers that be are so skilled, so insidious and so ubiquitous that the average man on the street, including many professionals, is often so totally unaware of the selling-out of America that they are shocked in disbelief when the "possibility" of such monstrous abuses is mentioned in their presence. David Casper and Thomas Stone speak out forcefully against the abuses relating to our food and water supplies, and many others. They document their work and convincingly shine a light for all who have ears to hear and minds to grapple with these issues. These two men are modern-day prophets. Their logic is nothing short of brilliant; their research is impeccable, their conclusions inescapable. May God grant America, and the world, the courage to read *Modern Foods*, take action and, thus informed, save our health from certain destruction.

—Bob L. Owen, Ph. D., D. Sc.
Author of *Ask Dr. Bob How To Maintain Your Health*
and *Roger's Recovery from AIDS*

The facts that *Modern Foods* brings to light are things that I've known and worried about for many years. I first heard that the corporations were buying up all the rights to the seed banks and destroying them so that we can only buy genetically modified foods, and I added that to the soils being emptied of minerals. I realized that we are probably facing the end of the normal food supply if left unchecked. (It may already be too late!) This can only mean the destruction of the people, and the first sign of this is the chronic plagues that we are already experiencing. Study the facts in this book, and do something about these alarming issues—now!

—Ed McCabe, Author of the best-seller
Oxygen Therapies, and the newly-released (©2002)
Flood Your Body With Oxygen: Therapy for Our Polluted World.

Casper and Stone shine a well-deserved spotlight on the food industry hiding in the shadows, behind the pillars of government. An invaluable guide for making informed food choices. I highly recommend *Modern Foods* for all those who cherish long life and freedom from disease.

—Lee Hitchcox, D.C.
Author of *Long Life Now*

Dr Armando DeGuzman, MD,

Thank you for being one

MODERN
FOODS

Largo support. Be

blessed in <u>All</u> you do,

and in <u>All</u> your doings

be a blessing.

3 John 2

Dr Thomas Stone

MODERN FOODS

THE SABOTAGE OF EARTH'S FOOD SUPPLY

David Casper, M.A.
and
Thomas Stone, N.D., C.N.

Foreword by Jonathan V. Wright, M.D.

CenterPoint Press
San Diego, California

David Casper is a medical and health researcher and writer based in the Pacific Northwest. Mr. Casper holds a Master's Degree in the Social Sciences.

Thomas Stone is a holistic health practitioner whose Southern California practice is dedicated to a totally non-invasive approach to natural medicine. Dr. Stone is a naturopathic physician, a certified natural healthcare professional and a certified nutritionist.

If you would like to contact the authors,
you may write to them c/o CenterPoint Press,
PMB 143, 12463 Rancho Bernardo Road, San Diego, CA 92128.

CONTENTS

FOREWORD

If there were any doubt why the "organic food movement" has grown so dramatically over the past two decades, *Modern Foods* by David Casper and Thomas Stone shows us why. Not only is organically grown and processed food more tasty, more nutritious and better for our health, but it avoids nearly all the "dark side" of our food and water supply, the subject of the pages which follow.

Our food and water have undergone more unhealthful change in the last few generations than in the entire history of humanity on Earth, yet since we've all "grown up with it," it seems "normal" and relatively safe, even if not entirely natural. In the pages to follow, Casper and Stone bring us face-to-face with the enormity of these detrimental changes. In approximately 150 pages, they give us the most comprehensive yet concise and understandable recounting of what's *really* happened to our food and water that I've read anywhere. For those who want to dig deeper for information on their own, the authors have included references in the text, and appended another nine pages of nothing but references.

Modern Foods not only tells us *what* has happened to our food and water, but gives us an explanation of *why* and *how*, based on the authors' unusually clear understanding of the social trends and corrupt politics behind the deterioration of our nation's food and water supplies. While America's political liberals and socialists have blamed "Big Corporations" for most of our social and political problems, and America's "right wing" blames "Big Government," Casper and Stone reveal the collusion (both in public and behind the scenes) between Big Corporations and Big Government that's brought us to the present mess. While I don't agree with 100% of their political analyses and conclusions, the vast majority is "right on." It's far closer to what I believe to be an accurate picture than anything I've read to date.

What can we do? Writing more laws and regulations and strengthening existing regulatory agencies or creating new ones *will not help!* Economic and social historians have repeatedly observed that regulatory agencies are inevitably "captured" by the very industries they're intended to regulate. The "revolving door" for upper-level managers between the Food and Drug Administration and the pharmaceutical industry is a legendary and well-documented example of this "capture." Appealing to any government agency is generally useless unless one can afford an army of well-paid attorneys, and unfortunately Congress allows most regulatory agencies to continue on with whatever they wish to do with only occasional cursory oversight.

So what can any one person or family do about what's happened to our food and water supply? "Going organic" as much as possible is the best solution. Even though more expensive as food than the commercial "food" described by Casper and Stone, organically-grown food is the cheapest *real* "health insurance policy" anyone can buy! For growing children or adults growing older, "eating organic" pays more and more dividends in good health and enjoyment of life than any "health insurance policy." Whenever possible, we should grow at least some of our food (organically of course) and buy from local organic growers at "farmer's markets." And as it's often not possible to eat 100% organically, dietary supplementation with vitamins, minerals and herbs is mandatory for the best of health.

Once we've done as much as we can for ourselves and our families, we need to do our bit to restore America's food and water supply to a healthy condition. Although writing, calling, faxing, and e-mailing our members of Congress is necessary, it's often not helpful, as Congress appears to have been purchased long ago by the same giant financial interests that influence the regulatory agencies (both behind the scenes, of course). Private citizens' *direct action* groups are the best answer at this time. One that's scored some notable successes is *Food and Water, Inc.*, (1-800-EAT SAFE), 389 Vermont Route 215, Walden, Vermont, 05873, (USA), http://www.foodandwater.com.

Despite *Modern Foods'* descriptions of the mess our food and water supply is in, it isn't intended to scare us, but to motivate us to *do something about it*, first for ourselves and our families, and then for our country!

Jonathan V. Wright, M.D.
Medical Director
Tahoma Clinic
Kent, Washington, USA

Part One:
Gathering Perspective

* * * * * * * * *

What is, is. But what is is, is another question.
— David Casper

Chapter 1

THE FRAMEWORK

By the grace of God we are born into this world, and then we begin to eat. Perhaps mother's milk at first (what's mom been eating?), or perhaps it's some of the high-tech, store-bought infant formula you will read about later in this book. Typically, a steady diet of store-bought food begins the life of each new, modern being living in our modern culture, and this continues throughout childhood into adulthood. Modern beings, modern food. Seems like a good match—but not necessarily so.

In the old days perhaps mom, grandma or grandpa had their own garden and raised wholesome, nutritious foods. For most of us this is no longer the case. As citizens of the modern world *we rely upon others* to supply our food, most of which is completely different from that of our distant ancestors *and* recent relatives. This newly-acquired dependence upon others to supply healthy, nutritious foods has taken the important task of food production out of the hands of the individual and placed it squarely into the hands of other (unknown) people—actually, mostly large corporations. If we are observant, we will have noticed that accompanying the advent of modern civilization, illness and disease have followed closely in the footsteps of "progress." What is the extent of the connection between the food we eat and the level of illness and disease presently manifesting throughout Western culture? What are the problems associated with our modern food supply?

It is important not only to understand *what* happens, but the *why* and *how* of the story are equally as significant. For example, if we have a sack of rotten apples, it's important to understand that fact. *What's* wrong with the apples? They're rotten. On the other hand, to understand *why* they are rotten and *how* this situation came into being are important factors as well. Indeed, by understanding *why* and *how* situations occur, one is in a better position to effect *what* will happen in the future.

Most of the content of *Modern Foods* tackles the issues of what has happened to our food and water supplies—at the same time an interesting and disappointing story, as you shall soon see. However, chapters one and two take on the issues of why and how these circumstances have come into being. Armed with this information, people may wish to make changes for the better. To understand the *what*, *why* and *how* of modern food production on all three levels is to more thoroughly grasp the complete and total picture. Without a comprehensive understanding, effective solutions are likely no more than wishful thinking.

Obviously, most people wish the best for others in most matters of life. However, with regard to food production—a gigantic and massively lucrative business enterprise—it is dangerously naive to assume beneficent intentions of those who produce our foods, and of those who oversee its safety and nutritiousness. Where vast sums of money are at stake, corruption often lurks close by.

Whether from simple oversight, being over zealous to increase the profit margin, or as the result of less admirable intentions, it is a fact that those in control of our food supply have dropped the ball—on us. And it will take some effort to pry ourselves out from under this weight and determine how to dodge future threats.

Unfortunately for us, the full scope of the problems associated with modern foods isn't immediately obvious, as it often takes years or decades for the physical and mental signs of ill health and disease to manifest. It's similar to the story of the frog in boiling water. As the story goes, if you put a frog in boiling water, it will immediately hop out of the pot. But if you put the frog in cool, soothing water...and then slowly begin to increase the heat, the frog will fry. So it is with us. The ailments resulting from our compromised food supply creep upon us insidiously. Before you know it, it's got you!—you're either ill, expecting a visit from the Grim Reaper, or sprouting flowers. Much of this is tragedy which need never happen.

It is not necessary to compromise a nation's food supply in the drastic fashion that exists today based on the need to produce vast quantities of food for our increasingly large and growing nation, and world. Although the economic factor of producing "cheap food" has been used to justify the means and problemed results of production, other safer, technologically-advanced techniques of food production are currently available and have been demonstrated cost effective. In fact, they are much more cost effective in the long run than the techniques presently in use. Why then, do harmful methods of food production continue to be practiced in light of such clear evidence demonstrating their harmfulness to the physical and mental health of the public?

One principle causative factor responsible for bringing about the unfortunate state of our food supply is—greed, with accompanying unconsciousness—a blending of a type of ethical somnambulism, if you will, with the need to acquire wealth and power. This is not just greed and lack of consciousness on an individual level, but at the corporate level, often carefully thought out in the boardrooms and unemotionally put into practice. Truly, such examples of avarice illustrate the darker side of the economic structure of capitalism—the grand, unfinished economic experiment of both the 20th and now the beginning of the 21st Centuries. In fact, some would argue that little more than the word "capitalism" remains intact, while in practice the true economic structure of the U.S. and other Western countries—soon to be the world— is quite different indeed from the way it is usually perceived.

What has happened, in effect, is that throughout the better part of the last 100 years, groups of powerful people have developed business strategies behind the scenes with the intent of acquiring vast quantities of wealth and power at any expense. If this concept sounds familiar, no doubt it is because these same strategies have become practically synonymous with standard American business practices. So much so that many of us assume this is the way it always has been and the way it always should and shall be, with little knowledge or understanding of alternative practices and methods of behavior.

The present time represents a unique period in history. Only at this time in the evolution of culture have communications developed to such a degree that Earth truly has shrunk to the size of a global village. Along with this new interconnectedness has come centralization. For example, prior to the last 50-100 years, commerce was segmented and decentralized. Businesses were operated on a much smaller scale than today. A merchant would supply only his local area with product or service. Powerful people were more likely to operate within a smaller sphere of influence.

Times have changed, and so has the nature of business. Today, globalization is key. The largest businesses are trans-national, i.e., they operate with no special ties to any nation other than where the most profit can be generated. Unlike times past, the actions of these behemoths usually affect millions of people, and the stakes often can be high. A defective product or unwise policy can change the lives of multitudes, practically overnight.

What this means is that when mistakes are made, they are often big mistakes with dramatic and lasting consequences to large segments of society, possibly to civilization *en toto*. Society's high degree of susceptibility to and dependence on the structures and mores of megacorporations and their administrators (a fact that is not obvious to some, probably many) only emphasizes the need for citizens to be mindful of what transpires around them in the realms of politics, big business and social control—the principal factors affecting our food supply.

Modern Foods is one such "heads up," although there have been many others who have come forward to speak their piece. Even recently, *Fast Food Nation: The Dark Side of the All-American Meal* (©2001) has made its way to *The New York Times* Best Seller's List. Also recently published is *The Crazy Makers: How the Food Industry Is Destroying Our Brains and Harming Our Children* (©2000). Another recent offering is *Slaughterhouse: The Shocking Story of Greed, Neglect and Inhumane Treatment Inside the U.S. Meat Industry* (©1997); and there are others. These books are notable efforts, but efforts which reach a minimal number of people compared to the total number of eaters, i.e., all those who need to hear the story. (Selection to *The New York Times* Best Seller's List, for example, can require as few as 30,000 sales).

Fortunate for us we live in the modern age where communication reigns. We'll just put the word out on television and soon everyone will be well informed. After Dan Rather, Peter Jennings, Tom Brokaw and Ted Koppel snitch on these bad guys—these blundering businessmen—they'll be corporate toast. But what's wrong with that picture? Why doesn't this happen? Why aren't we barraged by announcement after announcement, program after program, telling us, teaching us about simple things such as the food we eat—giving us the accurate information needed to make informed decisions?

True, there are occasional exposés. But why isn't the publicity generated by the concerned media so pervasive that offending companies would be socially shamed into sustainable, conscious policies? And if not an outcome so altruistic, then at least the offending companies would understand the public has been told, the information is out, and everyone knows their product is harmful, deficient or otherwise less than acceptable. After all, if a person owns a company which produces a product everyone else knows is defective in some fashion, how misguided that person or company would be to continue producing the product!

The situation becomes more understandable realizing the media are huge corporations as well, often having vested interests in companies such as those which produce food (and everything else). There are behind-the-scenes interlocking relationships between thousands upon thousands of corporations so that it is difficult to keep track of who owns whom and who partners with whom. Rest assured though, these Goliaths watch each others' backs.

We live in an era where communication reigns, but only certain things can be said. We do have freedom of speech, but only to a certain level and in certain situations. Witness Oprah Winfrey's recent court battle brought about as the result of the Agricultural Product Disparagement Laws, presently on the books in roughly a dozen states. This law makes it illegal to speak disparagingly about food products. Oprah came face-to-face with this law in 1996 when she remarked on her television show that her understanding of the dangers related to eating beef prevented her from eating any more burgers. The Texas Beef Group, et al, quickly brought legal action against her.

If Oprah would have lost this case, which she did not, the food giants would have tightened the noose one notch tighter— from, "Don't speak badly about our bananas," to perhaps, "Don't look askance at our bananas." What a convenient arrangement— produce an inferior product and then go about having laws passed preventing the public from speaking disparagingly about the product. Individually, we can speak freely, generally. Having access to a means of voicing our views on a national or international level is an entirely different matter. Even if we do gain such access, we must be prepared to meet retaliation.

In many other situations, freedom of speech is a *non-issue* because information is being intentionally and successfully sequestered to the extent that the public *doesn't realize certain issues even exist*. On the other hand, many people intentionally harbor themselves from information in an effort to make life more comfortable. Experience has shown this tactic to be effective, but only in the short term.

Policies of industrial conglomerates can and often do dominate all other concerns. For many Americans it's difficult to accept that this dominance is *actually* happening, would be *allowed* to happen, or is *even possible*. "We would be told; we would be warned." The alarm has indeed been sounded by many prominent people on "the inside," people whose lifetimes have been spent learning about their individual niche subject in areas such as the news media, the military, industry, politics, and the like.

One such insider was (U.S. Army General) Dwight D. Eisenhower, the 34th President of the United States. In his Farewell Radio and Television Address to the American People in 1961, Eisenhower warned his fellow countrymen about the potential dangers of what he called the "militaryindustrial complex," a term which is now in everyday use.

> This conjunction of an immense military establishment and a large arms industry is new in the American experience. The total influence – economic, political, even spiritual – is felt in every city, every Statehouse, every office of the Federal government. We recognize the imperative need for this development. Yet we must not fail to comprehend its grave implications...In the councils of government, we must guard against the acquisition of unwarranted influence, whether sought or unsought, by the militaryindustrial complex. The potential for the disastrous rise of misplaced power exists and will persist. We must never let the weight of this combination endanger our liberties or democratic processes.

> We should take nothing for granted. *Only an alert and knowledgeable citizenry* [emphasis added] can compel the proper meshing of the huge industrial and military machinery of defense with our peaceful methods and goals, so that security and liberty may prosper together.

> Akin to, and largely responsible for the sweeping changes in our industrial-military posture, has been the technological revolution during recent decades...in holding scientific research and discovery in respect, as we should, *we must also be alert to the equal and opposite danger that public policy could itself become the captive of a scientifictechnological elite* [emphasis added].[1]

These are prophetic words coming from someone "in the know," indeed, someone at the very top. Eisenhower foresaw the potential "capture" of public policy by these two mega-forces even while they were in their (relative) adolescence. Today, that *potential* capture has manifested into the ugly reality of full-blown adulthood—posing a threat not only to the U.S., but the entire world. One example of this is France's recent complaint regarding the U.S.'s use of the Echelon (keyword search: "echelon") satellite and ground-based electronic eavesdropping network to engage in acts of industrial espionage. On a larger scale, the ramifications of the military-industrial complex can be observed by witnessing its persistent preoccupation with global petroleum reserves in such areas as the Middle East (Iraq), Africa (Somalia) and Central Asia (Afghanistan).

General Eisenhower should have taken a lesson from one of his predecessors in arms, Marine Corps Major General Smedley D. Butler. A two-time Medal of Honor recipient (1914 and 1917), General Butler rose through the ranks to become a legend in his own time. Butler had acquired so much insight throughout his thirty-three year career as a soldier that in 1933 when he spoke of his experiences to an American Legion Convention in Connecticut, he was reasonably certain of his conclusions. Said Butler:

> A racket is best described, I believe, as something that is not what it seems to the majority of people. Only a small inside group knows what it is about. It is conducted for the benefit of the very few at the expense of the masses...

> The trouble with America is that when the dollar only earns 6 percent over here, then it gets restless and goes overseas to get 100 percent. Then the flag follows the dollar and the soldiers follow the flag.

> I wouldn't go to war again as I have done to protect some lousy investment of the bankers. There are only two things we should fight for. One is the defense of our homes and the other is the Bill of Rights. War for any other reason is simply a racket.

> There isn't a trick in the racketeering bag that the military gang is blind to. It has its 'finger men' to point out enemies, its 'muscle

men' to destroy enemies, its 'brain men' to plan war preparations and a 'Big Boss', Super-Nationalistic-Capitalism...

I spent thirty-three years and four months in active military service as a member of this country's most agile military force, the Marine Corps. I served in all commissioned ranks from Second Lieutenant to Major General. And during that period, I spent most of my time being a high class muscle-man for Big Business, for Wall Street and for the Bankers. In short, I was a racketeer, a gangster for capitalism...

I helped make Honduras "right" for American fruit companies in 1903. I helped make Mexico, especially Tampico, safe for American oil interests [Standard Oil] in 1914. I helped make Haiti and Cuba a decent place for the National City Bank boys to collect revenues in [now CitiBank; begun by William Rockefeller, brother of John D. Rockefeller, Sr.]. I helped in the raping of half a dozen Central American republics for the benefits of Wall Street. The record of racketeering is long. I helped purify Nicaragua for the international banking house of Brown Brothers in 1909-1912 [later, Brown Brothers Harriman, business partner of Prescott Bush, President George W. Bush's grandfather]. I brought light to the Dominican Republic for American sugar interests in 1916. In China I helped to see to it that Standard Oil [now Exxon; begun by J.D. Rockefeller, Sr.] went its way unmolested.

During those years, I had, as the boys in the back room would say, a swell racket. Looking back on it, I feel that I could have given Al Capone a few hints. The best he could do was to operate his racket in three districts. I operated on three continents.[2]

According to General Butler, a racket is an enterprise whose true purpose is known only to a small, select group of insiders, the others being led to draw different conclusions altogether—for the sole benefit of the few, to the detriment of the many. If this definition sounds familiar, it is because some have dared call this *conspiracy*. The American public's view of conspiracy represents one of the most stunning victories of the "thought police" over the minds of the public.

The word "conspiracy" has been made so unpalatable to the American public that one is viewed by his peers as "odd" (to say the least) to believe such things as conspiracies could exist in reality. In the case of the food disparagement issues, laws had to be enacted to curb the outspoken behavior of the public. But in the case of persons conspiring amongst themselves to attain some hidden agenda, no laws need be passed in our society to silence public discussion, because the public has been *conditioned to police itself*—in this instance and in many others. (For more interesting reading on this and related subjects, Jim Redden's recent book *Snitch Culture: How Citizens Are Turned into the Eyes and Ears of the State*, provides some interesting insights.)

The term conspiracy, in fact, would be incomplete without its proper suffix, "theory." We are to believe that conspiracies are so improbable they are to be viewed (labeled) as mere theory—only rants and ravings of the fanciful and paranoid. As long as an issue remains theoretical, the connotation is that it cannot be accepted as fact until it is either proved or disproved sometime in the future, regardless of the weight of the present evidence. George Orwell, author of the classics *1984* and *Animal Farm*, warned against such clever use of verbiage to disguise true intentions. "Political language is designed to make lies sound truthful and murder respectable, and to give an appearance of solidity to pure wind," said Orwell.

A brief review of recent U.S. history shows the use of the word "conspiracy" has not always brought such disfavor. Following the turn of the 20th Century, from around 1900 to 1910, significant public and political outcry had begun against what were seen by many as the excesses of big business. It was at this time, in fact, that many of the larger companies had begun to consolidate, and form powerful strategic alliances which were later to become monopolies—constructs and relationships that remain in existence even today, although they presently hide behind vast mazes of legal structures and are largely impervious to public (or political) investigation. In 1906, the U.S. government charged John D. Rockefeller Sr.'s Standard Oil Company with violating the Sherman Anti-Trust Act (dealing with the improper formation of monopolies). On May 15, 1911 the U.S. Supreme Court issued a clearly-worded verdict against Standard Oil, including the following,

> Seven men and a corporate machine have conspired against their fellow citizens. For the safety of the Republic we now decree that this dangerous conspiracy must be ended...[3]

And ended it was, although the disintegration of Standard Oil only proved to be a boon (and a boom) to the Rockefellers. Of the 33 oil companies formed following the breakup of Standard, Rockefeller retained roughly 25% ownership in them all. Of the companies that formed following Standard's dissolution, eight retained the name "Standard Oil." Standard Oil of New York later became Mobil Oil Corporation; by 1984, Standard Oil of California and Standard of Kentucky had become the Chevron Corporation; Standard Oil of Indiana merged with Standard of Nebraska and Kansas to become The Amoco Corporation in 1985; and in 1972 Standard Oil of New Jersey changed its name to Exxon. Atlantic-Richfield, Buckeye Pipe Line, Pennzoil, and Union Tank Car Company complete the list of "former" Standard Oil companies.[4] Only recently, Exxon and Mobile (re-) merged into what insiders have called the $75 billion "Rockefeller's revenge."[5]

The Rockefeller involvement in monopolistic business practices represents only one example amongst a treasure trove of others, involving powerful people, powerful families and powerful governmental agencies that have stood behind such practices, and still do, even though there are occasional political gestures intended to placate the public—such as the Supreme Court's 1911 decision that only brought more wealth into the already-overflowing coffers of John D. Rockefeller, Sr.

In a more contemporary example of monopolistic business practices and the business/government connection as they relate to the food industry, in July of 1999 the Clinton administration approved (over the objections of attorneys general from farm states, the Farmers Union, and consumer and green groups) the amalgamation of the two largest grain-trading companies in the United States, Cargill, Inc. (allied with Monsanto—now Pharmacia) and

Continental Grain, Inc. Together, it is estimated the two companies, now one, controll 94% of the soybean and 53% of the corn market. Following the merger, Cargill also controls more than 40% of all U.S. corn exports, one third of all soybean exports and over 20% of all wheat exports. According to Cargill executives, it is not unrealistic to expect the company will grow at a rate of 100% every five years.[6] Now that's progress!

Continuing on the glutenous roll of amalgamation, in the midwestern U.S., 75% of the sheep are slaughtered by ConAgra, Superior Packing, High Country and Denver Lamb. Eighty percent of beef cattle are slaughtered by IPB, ConAgra, Cargill and Farmland Beef. Sixty percent of the hogs are slaughtered by Cargill, Murphy Family Farms, Carroll's Foods and Smithland Foods. Only six companies process 50% of the nation's chickens: Tyson Foods, Gold Kist, Perdue Farms, Pilgram's Pride, ConAgra Poultry and Cargill. Over 75% of all U.S. corn, wheat and soybeans are sold to three companies: Cargill, Archer Daniels Midland (ADM, allied with Novartis, the Swiss conglomerate that includes Sandoz and Ciba-Geigy) and Bunge.[7]

William Heffernan, a professor of rural sociology at the University of Missouri, has stated that once you untangle the web of subsidiaries, mergers, joint ventures, partnerships, side agreements, marketing arrangements and alliances, "three food chains dominate the global food-production system"—Cargill/Monsanto(Pharmacia), ConAgra and Novartis/ADM.[8] Welcome to the New World Food Order!

Recent former CEO of Archer Daniels Midland, Dwayne Andreas, boasted to Reuters news service that he wanted to make ADM the world's dominant agricultural firm because there's simply nothing more powerful than controlling the world's food supply. Andreas stated that agribusiness is even more powerful than the petroleum industry. (And we have recently observed how the world-wide oil industry is of tantamount importance in world affairs; after all, wars are fought over such things...)

As for General Butler, who for most of his soldiering career—by his own admission—represented the leading edge of the corporate attack force, his remarks regarding his experiences as a soldier offer a unique and valuable historical perspective to this book, in that a portion of his career was engaged in paving the way for American fruit, sugar and other food-industry interests. Earlier, it was mentioned that the principal factors affecting our food supply are politics, big business, and social control. General Butler's forthrightness about this unique point in history helps to elucidate this reality. It also demonstrates the degree of interconnectedness between the many segments of power; when they move, they are able to move as one. The sheer amount of power acquired by these commercial interests over at least the last 100 years is astounding.

Why would such a courageous citizen/soldier as General Butler support policies and practices which were so clearly out-of-line with his convictions? Butler's comments on this issue are sobering:

> It may seem odd for me, a military man to adopt such [views]. Truthfulness compels me to...I suspected I was just part of a racket at the time. Now I am sure of it. Like all members of the military profession, I never had a thought of my own until I left the service. My mental faculties remained in suspended animation while I obeyed the orders of higher-ups.[9]

How owners and managers of huge corporations—not to mention military and political leaders—can lose sight of the harmful consequences of their actions becomes more transparent with Butler's insights. Due to many factors such as greed, peer pressure, family pressure, the stress of fast-paced living, etc., important matters become severely compromised and sometimes forgotten. One's life becomes relegated to going with the flow, wherever it may lead. This is the path of least social (translate: mental) resistance, something at which some of us have become well practiced. All too often it is all too easy to follow this path, whether we be soldiers, sailors, tinkers, politicians or homemakers. The practice of such behavior is what has allowed humanity to approach the edge of the cliff in areas such as food, water, air and the environment in general.

Because we are in the middle of it, we often lose sight of the fact that the so-called high-tech revolution is only a recent phenomenon. For all practical considerations it has happened only once, at least only once in our lifetimes, and it is a revolution that is presently ongoing. Because it has only happened once, and then only recently, humanity has had precious little experience dealing with the social changes and upheaval resulting in its wake. If our culture had gone through ten such upheavals in the past, or 20 or 30, it is reasonable to assume that as a society, as a world civilization, we would be closer to discovering *what really works*. But we are new at this—mere children at these tasks—and there is much we don't presently understand. We always like to believe the answers are close at hand, but the fact is that humans and our cultures are still works in progress. After all, America itself, as a culture, is just over 200 years into her experiment of free government—and many insiders don't like the odds for a copacetic conclusion.

When a child commits a blunder for the first time, it would be imprudent of the parent to punish that child. Perhaps we as citizens, voters and consumers should exercise some restraint and understanding when it comes to the big experiment of our modern, corporate food supply. Never before has the need to feed so many people been so great, and the world population continues to climb. Presently, the top 100 or so companies that produce the bulk of America's modern foods are prospering, and supplying the food needs of our culture in terms of quantity. This is a good thing for which these businesses should be commended. Food in America is plentiful, at least if you can pay for it.

As the child matures into adulthood, however, it is expected to modify many of its earlier practices which over time have come to be seen as worthy of change. As a person matures, so too should the behavior. Most would agree that true, civilized behavior incorporates—at the least—not harming others. As a child, transgressions can be forgiven. The young require leeway to grow. As adults, responsibility for one's actions comes into play.

The acquisition of wealth is seen by most as a good thing, and rightly so—but only to a degree. When serious physical and mental harm are the result of the means of accruing astonishingly vast segments of wealth within a society, throughout the entire globe, the line has been crossed and changes should be made. The corporate food giants have been at their game for many decades—at least 50-100 years. During this time a corporate culture has grown in the United States and the world whose behavior requires modification. If the corporate culture ever doubted whether it is time to modify its harmful business practices it should take an honest, sober look around at the present state of the world—including the food supply—wake up, and smell the coffee. It is time to develop more positive strategies that assist people instead of harming them, and are sustainable into the future. There was no better time to do this than yesterday. There is no better time than now. Without change, there may be no more time.

Americans don't like bad news. No one does. It's simply the way life is. On the other hand, a heads-up alert can be a lifesaving event. Understand that such an alert is actually an important *part of the solution*—it is *the first step*. Without information, a person becomes a *non-factor*, a *non-participant*. Non-participants do not effect change. They are affected by it, and moved at its fancy.

All one need do to be a participant is to have a basic understanding of some of the real issues that have the power to bring about real changes in our real lives. Not that we all must write books or be activists. On the contrary. All that is required are some basic insights into the world around us. The simple question is, "Do you want a chance to have a voice in the social and political policies which change our lives—or not?" Are we to be informed citizens, or holders of the belief that "ignorance is bliss?" If it is the latter, a rude surprise is destined to await. It is only when the various sides of issues are understood that informed decisions about factors which influence life's everyday affairs can be made. In the words of philosopher Alfred North Whitehead, "Where attainable knowledge could have changed the issue, ignorance has the guilt of vice."

For further research on the above topics, the following resources are recommended: Professor Howard Zinn's classic book, *A People's History of the United States*; Journalist Jim Marrs penetrating exposé, *Rule By Secrecy* (www.jimmarrs.com); Radio host Jeff Rense's Web site—particularly the current and archived articles and interviews at www.rense.com; Three 45-minute audio cassettes from American Media are also recommended: *Capitalist Conspiracy: An Inside View of International Banking*; *Wall Street and the Rise of Communism*; and *From Major Jordan's Diaries* (800-595-6596); Also, *The Money Masters: How International Bankers Gained Control of America* (www.themoneymasters.com; 888-843-7568).

As this chapter comes to a close, the authors would like to make several points about what you will find in the pages that follow—and what you won't. First, this writing is not intended to be an all-inclusive discourse on specific food products or classes of foods. You cannot look up items in the Index as you could in an encyclopedic-style text. For example, we do not discuss peanut butter, corn, or apple pie, *per se.*

Further, we have not intended to provide a complete and exhaustive treatise on the various topics discussed. After all, entire books have been written on virtually every subject discussed within these pages. Rather, our approach has been to touch upon a broad variety of topics and attempt to show how they interrelate, how they flow; what are the true intentions of the people involved, and what is the real meaning behind their words. In the end, we hope you will be left with a perspective that is greater than the sum of the parts presented. At the same time, in the interest of "accessability," we have made a conscious effort to keep the book to a manageable length that won't be burdensome to the average reader. In fact, we believe most books contain a lot of superfluous "padding" generated merely to fill pages. Not so with *Modern Foods*. You are guaranteed at least one thrill per page—or your money back.

Secondly, the subtitle of the book is *The Sabotage of Earth's Food Supply*, not *America's*, or *the United States'*, or any other specific country. Even though most of the cited documentation refers specifically to the United States, the high degree of business interconnectedness existing throughout the world today makes it very difficult to contain the problem of our contaminated and generally "low-class," modern food supply within any particular country's geographical borders. It's a global problem. Numerous examples of this are cited within the book. Where will it all end—sharing technology, partnering, consolidation, aggregation, monopolization? You guess what comes next.

Also, please don't overlook *Part Three: The Solutions*. For those who read from the back of the book to the front, this won't be a problem. However, if you are a discerning reader committed to understanding the issues we discuss on a more intimate level, we suggest you read straight through to the end—keeping in mind there are some good suggestions waiting for you toward the end of the book. Although we tell you about the problems—the subject of the next sections—we also make some practical suggestions about how to avoid virtually all of the problems discussed, at least the food-related ones. We also provide links to many sources of information for further study, should you choose to pursue these issues further.

PART TWO: THE PROBLEMS

* * * * * * * *

*After a person is shown the truth, it is up to
that person to accept it, or to continue
wishing it were some other way.*

— Thomas Stone

Chapter Two

THE BETRAYAL

From the time of the early hunters and gatherers who foraged for their next meal, to the cultures that eventually cultivated both food crops and livestock, man's acquisition of food and water has always been of singular importance. Although the human diet varied somewhat from geographic location to location depending on the availability of certain food stuffs and the particular preferences of different cultures, the quantity and easy accessability of the food supply have always been issues of great concern, and understandably so.

Only recently has this constant struggle to acquire food been somewhat abated, at least for many in the Western world. Most people living in the United States—and particularly those living in highly-populated, urban areas—have access to the most varied and plentiful supply of food in the history of modern man. However, the nature of the foods themselves has changed considerably.

For millennia—at least hundreds of thousands if not millions of years—humans have eaten plants and to some extent the flesh of animals, either wild-growing or cultivated. Over time, the ingenuity of man has created various means of producing vast amounts of food in order to feed Earth's increasingly-growing population. Although the quantity of the food supply has never been greater than today, the foods consumed by our ancestors were relatively pure and natural (i.e., unadulterated) in comparison to our present-day food supply. In other words, there has been a trade-off—quality for quantity.

During the past 100 years or so, the American (Western) diet has changed so radically that virtually no one younger than an octogenarian can remember what the human diet consisted of prior to the advent of modern foods of convenience. The process of eating has remained unchanged. The substances still enter through the orifice directly below the nose; they are chewed; then swallowed. Nothing has changed here. The nature of the food stuffs, however, has changed drastically. So much has it changed that those substances presently masquerading as foods no longer maintain human life at an optimal level—not even at an advantageous level; not even at an acceptable level; not even at a level sufficient to maintain the body in a state free from illness and disease. This is a remarkable circumstance given the fact that we depend on these vital substances for our very existence.

Air, water and food are the three most vital necessities of man. First and foremost, before other needs are considered, these basic requirements must be fulfilled. Of these three, air is the most vital. Without air, a person can survive only for minutes. The second most vital necessity, water, comprises approximately two thirds of the human body and about 90% of the brain. Life cannot be sustained for more than several days without rehydrating the body with liquid. Although man can abstain from eating for many days, the continued absence of food ultimately leads to death.

Yet, in order to maintain ourselves in a state of *optimal* health, these three vital nutrients must attain at least a minimal level of purity. Creation has offered these necessities as an uncontaminated resource, and so they should be maintained. Any substantial degree of adulteration will be accompanied by ill health and disease, and decrease our capacity to achieve life's fulfillments. One would think it only reasonable that our air, water and food supplies be kept pure and pristine, lest there be dire consequences to both the individual and society at large. To not do so would be to undermine in the crudest way the foundation upon which our lives depend.

A relatively small number of people have been entrusted to maintain for all of us the wholesomeness of these life-sustaining resources, and we depend upon them to fulfill this most important obligation. Should they fail in the performance of their duties, the consequences would be catastrophic and widespread. Failure—the degradation of life's most vital necessities—would reduce man to a mere shadow of his capabilities.

Unfortunately, as many are well aware, the keepers of the public trust have failed and the Earth, including human life, is challenged on almost every front by life-threatening pollution. An example of this is the very air we breathe, now polluted to a considerable extent. Each one of us breathes hundreds of gallons of air every day, yet the air of our fast-paced societies contains many toxic chemicals. Every year in the United States, more than 130 million tons of noxious chemicals are released into the atmosphere—chemicals such as carbon monoxide, hydrocarbons, nitrogen oxides and sulfur oxides. Each person living in New York City, for example, may inhale the equivalent of as much as 700 pounds of chemicals per year.[1]

The water we drink and bathe in fares little better. About 50% of our usable water comes from ground water, which is fresh water that percolates through the soil and is held in underground aquifers. The other 50% of our usable water is sourced from rivers, streams and reservoirs. Unfortunately, both of these resources have been heavily polluted by industrialization, rendering our water supplies contaminated and toxic.

As an example of the severity of the problem, the U.S. Environmental Protection Agency (EPA) recently estimated that throughout this country an average of *50 billion gallons* of liquid industrial wastes are disposed of in ponds, lagoons and other surface reservoirs *on a daily basis*. These contaminants include synthetic chemicals such as cleansers, fertilizers, pesticides (including insecticides and herbicides), solvents as well as thousands of other agricultural, household and industrial chemicals including antibiotics and pharmaceutical drugs.

Water cannot be separated from food, as it provides nourishment to both the food crops and the animals raised for food consumption. Many foods are also washed with water in preparation for eating. Contamination of the water supply affects every aspect of food consumption.

Neither has our food supply been spared contamination from toxic substances added directly to the foods during manufacture, and in other ways. The adulterated condition of our current food supply is beyond what most people understand, and worse than most would want to believe possible.

In the United States, the alphabet soup of government agencies responsible for overseeing the safety of the food supply are: the Food and Drug Administration (FDA), the Department of Agriculture (USDA), the Department of Health and Human Services (HHS) and the Environmental Protection Agency (EPA). The FDA is the principal agency responsible for food safety, although there is some overlap of functions between these agencies. How is it possible the food supply could be anything but pure and pristine when not one but several agencies are standing guard to protect the foods from contamination?

The answer to this question involves several issues. On the one hand, the FDA is an agency whose resources are severely overtaxed. The agency is grossly underfunded and understaffed. Presently there are roughly 1,400 FDA inspectors tasked with inspecting some 100,000 food, animal drug, human drug, radiological, medical device and cosmetic companies.[2] According to the November 24, 1997 issue of *U.S. News and World Report*,[3] 700 FDA inspectors and laboratory workers monitor 53,000 food-processing plants as well as all imported produce. The level of funding for the agency is an anachronism. Given their limited resources, the FDA cannot possibly maintain adequate surveillance over the burgeoning food industry.

This historical lack of capability within the FDA has been acknowledged over a span of decades by leading officials within the agency itself. In 1957, the *Food, Drug and Cosmetic Law Journal* reported a statement made by former FDA Commissioner George P. Larrick:

> We have had some very narrow escapes because of the use of additives that had no place in foods. It is inconceivable that this country should continue to expose itself indefinitely to the risks inherent in the present scheme of food control.[4]

In 1970, *The New York Times* reported a statement made by former FDA Commissioner Dr. Herbert Ley, Jr.:

> What disturbs me is that people think the Food and Drug Administration is protecting them. It isn't. What the FDA is doing and what people think they are doing are as different as night and day.[5]

In 1989, the following statement by former FDA Commissioner Frank Young, M.D., Ph.D., appeared in *An FDA Consumer Special Report*:

> Unfortunately, microbial contamination and outbreaks of food-borne illnesses have continued at an alarming rate. According to estimates by our own FDA scientists, between 21 million and 81 million cases of food-borne diarrheal disease occur annually in the United States.[6]

Adding insult to injury, in 1991 an Advisory Committee to the FDA released their report, the Edwards Committee Report, named after its most distinguished member, former FDA Commissioner Dr. Charles Edwards. Among the Committee's conclusions was the following:

> The American public fully expects...a food supply which is not only safe, but also wholesome, and one that comes with complete instructions as to how the right foods can promote longer and healthier lives. Neither one of these objectives is being achieved under the present circumstances at the FDA.[7]

These unfortunate circumstances within the FDA as the result of lack of funding are understandable, although this does not in any way lessen the seriousness of the problem. Each day, the contamination of our food and water continues unabated.

On the other hand there is another, more sinister aspect to the problem of our contaminated food supply. At the root of this second aspect is the proverbial corporate quest to increase profitability, as discussed in Chapter One. Maximized profitability is a motive with which many in the Western world may sympathize. However, in the case of food production, maximized profitability has become practically synonymous with an unhealthy food supply.

The founder of the U.S. Food and Drug Administration, then called the Bureau of Chemistry, was Harvey W. Wiley, M.D. Dr. Wiley was nobly concerned with the purity of the American food supply and those whose task it was to protect it from contamination. He was the architect of the nation's first Pure Food and Drug Law enacted in 1906, also referred to as The Wiley Act.

Dr. Wiley's intention was to reform certain aspects of the food manufacturing industry. He led the fight against food additives, and among many other reforms sought to declare refined and bleached flour products as adulterated foods and thereby prohibited from interstate transport. Dr. Wiley resigned in disgust in 1912 due to pressures brought to bear by the food and pharmaceutical industries. He was so concerned about the potential dangers of these two industries that in 1929 he published his memoirs entitled *The History of a Crime Against the Food Law: The Amazing Story of the National Food and Drug Law Intended to Protect the Health of the People, Perverted to Protect Adulteration of Foods and Drugs*. Dr. Wiley died less than a year after his book was published, and within weeks the book "vanished from libraries and bookshops around the nation."[8] Dr. Wiley wrote:

> There is a distinct tendency to put regulations and rules for the enforcement of law into the hands of industries engaged in food and drug activities...I consider this one of the most pernicious threats to

pure foods and drugs. Business is making rapid strides in the control of all our affairs. When we permit business in general to regulate the quality and character of our food and drug supplies, we are treading upon very dangerous ground.[9]

The history of the domination of the food industry by a handful of conglomerates is at the same time fascinating and revealing. During the early 1920s, a few large corporations dominated the meat-packing, sugar and flour-milling industries. As the decade progressed the dairy, baking, tropical fruit and breakfast cereal segments of food production were consolidated. By the end of the decade, two massive corporate conglomerates emerged: General Foods and Standard Brands, each having consumed scores of other companies in their climb to the top. By the late 1960s and early 1970s, roughly 100 corporations controlled almost all of the U.S. food manufacturing industry.[10]

In a 1975 article published in the *Progressive*, industry analyst Daniel Zwerdling reported that among the major sectors of food production controlled in 1974 by only four companies were: breakfast cereals (90% of sales), canned goods (80%), bread and prepared flour (75%), dairy products (70%), baking (65%), fluid milk (65%), sugar (65%) and processed meats (56%). Campbell's soup sold 90% of America's soup.[11] This massive consolidation on the part of the food industry did not occur without its casualties, not the least of which was the heavy toll taken on the American farmer. Since the 1930s, more than three million small family farmers have been forced off the land by policies favoring agribusiness conglomerates.[12]

[Authors' note: It is interesting to observe that a similar process of consolidation occurred within many other industries during the same 50 year time span between 1920 and 1970, and also during the preceding two decades. Other industries which formed conglomerates include the pharmaceutical industry, communications (television, radio and printed news), energy, chemical, transportation (air, land and sea), technologies, the military industrial complex and last but certainly not least, the banking industry. Today, a relatively *small circle of people* presently serve as directors and owners of many of these corporations, most being multi(trans)national, which function in interlocking cartel relationships. Many of these people move from the corporate boardroom(s) through a "revolving door" into the highest levels of government and political life, and vice versa.

In 1978, more than two decades ago, a congressional subcommittee investigated this phenomenon and published the report *Interlocking Directorates Among the Major U.S. Companies.* The subcommittee found there were 63 major corporations interlocked with each other through the Chase Manhattan Corporation, 81 corporations interlocked through J.P. Morgan and Co., Inc. and 80 companies interlocked through Manufacturers Hanover Corp. Most of these companies are household names such as Allied Chemical, American Airlines, American Aluminum Company (Alcoa), American Broadcasting Companies, American Express, AT&T, Avis and Avon Products, to name just some of the As.

The report further stated that the list of "selected New York financial institutions and major non-financial corporations" was being given "in order to appreciate the extensive routes of information and potential consensus which can take place in the boardrooms of the largest corporations." The report added that,

> ...those corporate boards with a great number of large vested interests represented may be able to establish industry and interindustry policies for the benefit of those interests and to the detriment of those not so fortunate as to be represented on the boards.[13]

To understand the significance of the extent of influence wielded by these corporations is to understand much of the geopolitical machinations of the 20th Century—and beyond. This recognition helps one piece together heretofore mysterious events that transpire within societies and in the lives of men, and furnishes one with predictive powers concerning future global events as well.]

In 1969, consumer advocate Ralph Nader appeared before the U.S. Senate's Select Committee on Nutrition and Human Needs. Food industry historian Harvey Levenstein comments:

> [Nader] charged that the food industry was dominated by immensely powerful oligopolies [controlled by a small number of companies] who cared only about selling their products, not about their nutritive value. Their "manipulative strategies" bilked the consumer; "the silent violence of their harmful food products" caused "erosion of the bodily processes, shortening of life or sudden death." Geneticists feared that "the river of chemicals that all of us use and breathe" might be causing genetic defects among the newborn. Yet the "skilled salesmen" of the food industries used "applied social science" to shape consumer preferences in order "to maximize sales and minimize costs no matter what the nutritional, toxic, carcinogenic, or mutagenic impact may be on humans or their progeny."[14]

Presently, the U.S. food-manufacturing industry accounts for over one trillion dollars in annual sales, most of which is generated by less than 100 corporations, and about 65% being generated by 50 corporations[15]—congealing into a handful of food chains that dominate global food production, as mentioned in Chapter One. The U.S. food-production industry is the largest business in North America, employing over 20 million people.[16] Industry analyst and food biochemist Paul Stitt, drawing from his years as a food scientist with Tenneco and the Quaker Oats Company, defines the problem as the "Conspiracy of the Sales Curve." In his book *Beating the Food Giants*, Stitt comments:

> What sells the best is what determines what will be produced and how it will be marketed. That's true for all industries, of course, but making sales increases the top priority is especially dangerous in the food industry...research efforts are aimed not at finding new products or improving old ones, but in cutting the cost of production. In corporate lingo, it's called "product differentiation" and in advertisements they call the product "new and improved." The result is a cheaper, less nutritious product that costs the consumer more.[17]

Chapter Three

Unhealthy Consequences

The radical changes in our food supply over the last 100 years have not come without significant consequences. If it weren't for these consequences, the great-tasting, endless variety of today's foods would be a joy, as many currently believe them to be. Little do we realize that many of the foods consumed daily are killing us—and making us crazy—even if slowly. For many in the Western world, the connection between diet and disease, both physical and mental, is not readily apparent. After all, who has told us about the dark side of one of our most enjoyable pastimes? Our parents? Our friends? And if and when they do, how often does the message fall on deaf or hesitant ears? Even when we begin to understand the importance of these issues, the taste buds continue to cast their many votes in favor of flavor.

It is only by recognizing the true extent of the problems associated with our modern food supply that one can begin to break away. First we have to understand, and then we must act—a largely uphill battle on both fronts; but as we shall see, one that is worth waging. As you read the illness and disease statistics below, burn these figures into your mind, and remember them and their importance *to you* as you forge through some of the less-than-pleasant details you may encounter in the pages that follow.

In the United States, the two leading causes of death are heart disease and cancer, with cancer expected to be the leading cause in the near future. According to the American Heart Association, 50% of all American men will die from heart disease. Nearly twice as many women die from this disease each year than from all forms of cancer combined. Cancer, the second leading cause of death, afflicts 50% of American men and 30% of women with some form of this invasive disease, according to the American Cancer Society.[1] Some health authorities estimate that by the year 2020, virtually all Americans will contract some type of cancer during their lifetimes.

Today, heart disease accounts for about 35% of all deaths in the U.S., while cancer accounts for roughly 25%.[2] In 1900, heart disease accounted for 8% of all deaths, and cancer about 3.5%. In other words, since 1900 the number of cases of heart disease has increased by 400%, and the number of cases of cancer by over 600%. Mathematically speaking, for a person living in the United States, *there is a 75% probability for men and more than a 50% probability for women of being afflicted during their lifetimes either with heart disease, cancer or both.* These are unacceptable odds, even for a confirmed gambler.

In 1900, heart attacks were so rare that most physicians spent their entire careers never having witnessed a single episode. The first mention of the term "heart failure" appeared in the medical literature in 1912.[3] By the early 1920s, heart disease had attained epidemic proportions, and by the 1950s it had become the leading cause of death. Presently, the disease supports a $40 billion per year industry.

Cancer is mentioned neither in the *Bible* nor the ancient Chinese *Yellow Emperor's Classic of Medicine,*[4] a medical treatise dating back some 3,000 years. Presently, the "c" word is the leading cause of death in middle-aged Americans between the ages of 35-55. It is also the leading cause of death in American children between the ages of 1-14,[5] having increased some 20% between the years 1950 to 1990. The most optimistic estimate is that cancer has been rising at an overall rate of at least 1% per year for the last 30 years.[6] According to the National Cancer Institute, more Americans die each year from cancer than combined mortalities from WWII, Korea and Vietnam.

The inescapable conclusion is that during the last 100 years, something unprecedented has occurred that has caused such a drastic increase in these two most pernicious diseases, as well as many lesser diseases and illnesses. This is confirmed by the present cost of health care in the U.S. which is over $1 trillion annually. Citizens of 15 other countries now have a longer life expectancy than U.S. residents. What clues are to be found that point to the causative factor(s) behind the skyrocketing escalation of disease?

One clue is that during the last 100 years our environment has changed drastically. Pollution, both external and internal, has risen to previously unimaginable levels. The air we breathe, the water we drink and the foods we eat today are substantially more toxic in comparison to levels experienced by our ancestors.

Another clue is found in certain unique cultures in remote areas of the globe where until recently the inhabitants lived a virtually pollution-free lifestyle. There are at least five such remote cultures whose members until recently routinely lived to be more than 100 years old, and some lived as long as 120-140 years. People of these cultures generally experienced an exceptional state of health, with no presence of diseases such as heart disease, cancer, immune dysfunction, diabetes or osteoporosis.[7] Residents of these societies lived in an environment of clean, unpolluted air; they drank clean, unpolluted water and ate simple, uncontaminated, unprocessed, unadulterated foods. In recent years modern civilization has encroached on these societies, and the health of their residents has degraded significantly.

Modern science has also sought to understand the causes of the rapid rise to prominence of such a wide variety of illness and disease. Most experts agree that virtually all types of debilitating medical conditions, with the exception of those of genetic origin, are related to environmental factors such as air pollution, water pollution and the pollution of our food supply. In fact—and here's the clincher—the Surgeon General reported in 1988 that *diet-related diseases account for nearly 70% of all deaths in the United States.*[8] ("Diet-related" means the diet is either the *principal* causative factor, or a *co-factor* which exerts its influence along with another factor or factors.) Stated another way, the foods you eat play a secret game of Russian roulette with your health, with roughly a 70% chance you will lose!

Not only do the problems manifest in a physical form of illness. There has been a steady rise in the incidence of mental illness as well, as is evidenced by the fact that more than 10% of the U.S. population has been diagnosed with some form of mental illness, with nearly 25% of adults experiencing a mental health crisis in a given year.[9] As many as 14% of American children experience at least one serious bout of depression before the age of 15.[10] The sharp increase in the incidence of psychiatric drug use further elucidates the growing mental health problems within the U.S. population—if not within the medical psychiatric community as well.

Since its introduction in 1991, the antidepressant Prozac® has assertively climbed to fifth place on the top-10 list of pharmaceuticals. From 1996-1997 alone, prescriptions for Prozac increased nearly 150%. Teenagers between 13-18 years of age used 148,000 prescriptions for Prozac in 1995 and 217,000 prescriptions in 1996, up nearly 50%. Children ages 6-12 used 51,000 prescriptions of Prozac in 1995 and 203,000 in 1996, up 209%. Sales of Zoloft,® another antidepressant, are hot on Prozac's tracks. In 1995, 155,000 prescriptions were sold to teenagers between the ages of 13-18, with 199,000 being sold to this same age group in 1996, up nearly one third. Children aged 6-12 used 33,000 prescriptions for Zoloft in 1995, and up about 40% to 46,000 prescriptions in 1996. Sales of Paxil,® yet another best-selling antidepressant, were up 48% in the 13-18 age group and up 113% in the 6-12 age group, during the same time period of 1995-1996.[11]

The pharmaceuticals Prozac, Zoloft, Paxil and Luvox® are part of a group of antidepressants known as *Selective Serotonin Reuptake Inhibitors* (SSRIs), which collectively account for over 40 million prescriptions annually, supporting a $3 billion annual industry.[12] Total sales of all categories of antidepressants account for over $7 billion annually. When it recently became clear that antidepressant sales to adults had begun to plateau, the manufacturers began looking for additional markets, and the teenage-and-below market apparently was too lucrative to overlook. By offering orange- and mint-flavored versions of these drugs, they are being made available to younger and younger children. These expanded new markets would seem to be just what the doctor ordered—at least as a palliative for the stockholders.

In passing it is also interesting to note that while the above-mentioned psychoactive drugs are intended to help people, all too often these drugs have the opposite effect. As an example, many of the highschool and other senseless shootings which have plagued the U.S. have involved the perpetrators' taking this SSRI group of drugs. The list of casualties includes such household names as Eric Harris (Columbine High School; total killed: 13, wounded: 23; Luvox); Mark Barton (Atlanta day trader; total killed or injured at two separate brokerage firms: 22; he also killed his wife and two children; Prozac was found in his car.); Brynn Hartman, wife of deceased *Saturday Night Live* comedian Phil Hartman, was also taking a prescription SSRI drug when she killed her husband, and then herself; and the list goes on. Heard that from your local (legal) drug vendor lately?

Pharmaceutical (prescription) drugs in general—products which many imbibe on a daily basis—can have significant problems attendant to their use. Notwithstanding their many valid and sometimes life-saving uses, (correctly-prescribed) prescription drugs account for over 100,000 U.S. deaths per year, according to the American Medical Association. In fact, prescription drug deaths rank as the fourth leading cause of U.S. deaths, behind heart attacks, cancer and strokes. An additional 7,000 U.S. deaths per year occur due to hospital errors in prescribing pharmaceutical medications.

Learn more about these issues at www.drugawareness.org, the Web site of the International Coalition for Drug Awareness; also recommended are Dr. Peter Breggin's many books including *Toxic Psychiatry* (©1991) and *Talking Back To Prozac* (©1995). You may also access his informative Web site at www.breggin.com.

With the preceding as an historical and informational backdrop, the following unpleasant details are brought to you courtesy of the food monopolies, their government minions, and their insatiable quest for increased profits, increased power, and increased control. Fasten your seat belt, strap your socks on and prepare yourself for an ugly sojourn into the inescapable reality of our poisoned food supply. Bon voyage!

Chapter Four

PROCESSED FOODS

Natural foods are foods such as fruits, vegetables, grains, legumes (peas and beans), nuts and seeds that have been grown without the use of adulterants such as pesticidal chemicals—and the large variety of dishes made from off-shoots and combinations of these food. Meats may also be included in this category. Most of our ancestors the world over consumed meats of different kinds, although in much smaller quantities than are consumed by people of contemporary Western cultures, and Americans in particular. The meats eaten by our ancestors were for the most part harvested from the wild, although some livestock was cultivated. In either case, the meats they consumed were far different from the production-line meats found in today's supermarkets.

Processed foods are foods that have undergone some type of alteration or modification, such as the addition of preservatives, flavorings, colorings or texturizers. Other examples of typical processing techniques include dehydrating, freezing, precooking, preserving, pasteurizing and packaging. Inevitably, these processes lead to a substantial reduction in the food value of the final product. Processing also includes the refining of grains such as the milling of wheat flour, a procedure that removes over half of each of the most essential nutrients such as amino acids, chromium, cobalt, copper, iron, manganese, molybdenum, oils, phosphorous, thiamine, zinc as well as other minerals and trace elements. During the process of milling and bleaching, the fiber-rich bran is removed, and the vitamin-containing germ (vitamins E and B complexes and trace minerals) are also removed.[1]

As early as the 1920s, the manufacture of processed foods was in full swing. The newly-formed conglomerates had gained their strong foothold, and sought ways of producing foods more cheaply. Following WWII, from 1949-1959, food chemists lost no time in focusing their talents on the development of over 400 new chemical additives for use within the processed food industry.[2] One of the key points of consideration in the manufacture of modern foods is the importance of extended shelf-life. Processed foods are more profitable because they last longer on the shelves. In fact, many modern foods have such extended shelf-lives they could be said to be "virtually immortal." Free from the problems of life-limited foods such as fruits and vegetables, manufactures are currently at liberty to produce designer foods capable of pushing "consumer hot buttons," as the industry lingo calls it. Extended shelf-life allows companies to centrally locate their manufacturing facilities and ship products almost anywhere on the planet (and perhaps someday beyond, as some corporate executives might hope. Many foods would do well in intergalactic space, as they're already in a near state of suspended animation).

Paul Stitt comments:

> An ever-increasing proportion of the food we eat is no longer even food but is now a conglomerate of high-priced chemistry experiments designed to simulate food. There are even chemicals like...Merlinex, "the silly putty of the food world," which takes the place of the real thing in everything from cheese to brownies...Ruined natural ingredients, plus sugar, salt, fat, and chemical additives. Put them all together, and what have you got? You've got tantalizing, phony foods that are high in refined carbohydrates and calories and

devoid of nutritional value. It's a recipe for destruction—the formula for "Can't Eat Just One."[3]

As you read the remainder of this chapter, please keep in mind that, due to the constraint of limited space, only two specific food categories are discussed—infant formula and baby food. These two categories were chosen because of the importance of emphasizing adequate nutrition during childhood. We also discuss several specific food items which are *ingredients* in practically all processed foods: margarine; fats and oils; sugar; artificial sweeteners; and salt.

The formative years—infancy through the toddler stage—represent the most nutritionally-critical period in the life of a human being. All of the body's critical systems and structures are forming, and require the proper building blocks to insure continued good health. Fortunately, Mother Nature has provided the ultimate jump-start—a self-contained, ready-to-serve source of just what baby needs. In modern times, however, many mothers have elected to bottle-feed their infants as an alternative to breast feeding. The manufacturers' descriptions of their various infant formulas sound wonderful—better than the real thing; better than what mom brings to the table.

Infant formula containing cow's milk is fraught with problems. A sizeable number of infants are intolerant or allergic to cow's milk. (About 30% of adults are lactose intollerant as well.) According to Dr. Walter Willett of the Harvard School of Public Health, the high protein content of milk could leach calcium from bones—a result that is opposite from what is generally assumed. Also, the consumption of cow's milk has been linked to allergies and iron-deficiency anemia in infants and children. Former Director of the Johns Hopkins University Department of Pediatrics, Dr. Frank Oski, reports in his book *Don't Drink Your Milk*, that milk consumption may play a significant role in the development of heart attacks and atherosclerosis.[4]

Additionally, the wholesomeness of factory-farmed milk is seriously in question. Later, in Chapter 6, you will encounter the problems associated with bovine-sourced byproducts such as milk. If you have an infant in the family, or are expecting one soon, pay particular attention to the discussion about the problems related to milk in general. It will become apparent that milk as an ingredient in infant formula poses significant long-term liabilities.

During the early 1960s, soy was introduced into infant formulas as an alternative to cow's milk. Although the plant was known as early as 1100 B.C. (Chou Dynasty, China), only the root of soy was used, and then only as a soil treatment. Later, following the discovery of fermentation, the Chinese made tempeh, miso and soy sauce from soybeans—but they did not eat unfermented soy because of the recognized toxins it contains. For example, soy contains inhibitors that can interfere with amino acid uptake and digestion. Also, soy contains substances known to depress thyroid functioning.

The modern soy product, whether it be infant formula or tofu, contains a substance called *soy protein isolate*. This isolate is the principal soy ingredient of soy products. Of interest is that soy protein isolate was never granted the FDA status of Generally Recognized As Safe (GRAS) because it was not in common use prior to 1958 when many substances were "grandfathered" into use under this system. Because the isolate does not have a GRAS status, the FDA guidelines require a formal step called "premarket approval" before non-GRAS substances are allowed to be marketed. Soy protein isolate has never obtained premarket approval from the FDA. What this means is that the principal ingredient in soy infant formula is not currently recognized as safe by the Food and Drug Administration. Further, the American Academy of Pediatrics recognizes that early exposure to soy protein isolate in infant formulas may be the principal contributing factor which causes allergies in both older children and adults.

In addition to being implicated in enzyme inhibition, thyroid malfunction and allergies, soy protein isolate contains high levels of powerful estrogen-like *isoflavones*. It was recently discovered that the average infant using soy-based formula receives six to eleven times the dosage of this substance than was found to cause hormonal effects in adult eaters of soy products. Researchers have found that babies fed exclusively on soy infant formula receive the equivalent estrogen dose of at least five birth control pills per day. There is no question of soy's overwhelming potential to affect early sexual development of the infant, including issues of sexual identity and early onset of puberty. Early onset of puberty has been linked to menstrual difficulties, infertility and breast cancer.[5] Further reading can be done at www.truthaboutsoy.com.

As the infant grows, more solid foods are introduced. These solid "baby foods" typically contain vegetables and/or meats. These foods are subject to contamination from the same sources as any other food, including both chemical and microbial contamination which are discussed in detail in following chapters. Because of the potent effects these contaminants can and do have upon a baby's growing body, parents are urged to pay particular attention to the quality of food their babies receive.

The Center for Science in the Public Interest has an excellent Web site covering a multiplicity of food-related topics, including processed foods. They also have the section "Protect Your Baby," which gives a great deal of relevant information of concern to parents. www.cspinet.org

Cereal. Breakfast cereal is an example of a processed food that manufacturers have invested multiple hundreds of millions of dollars to market, especially to children—their prime target market. Although ready-to-eat cold cereal has been with us since about 1900, the sugar-coated, pre-sweetened variety emerged in 1949. Most breakfast cereals are high in sugar content and low in nutritional value, if having any positive nutritional value at all. Kellogg's Sugar Smacks,® for example, contains about 55% sugar,[6] with many of the other cereals trailing close behind. These products would more properly be labeled as candy or confections rather than foods, although they are advertised as promoting vigor, strength and athleticism. It's sad to think that children, one group of people most requiring healthy foods, would be the focus of such intensive advertising campaigns. The fancy shapes—stars, moons, circles, crowns—and the bright colors leave little doubt to whom the advertising budgets are being directed. One top executive of a large cereal manufacturer is quoted as having said:

> It's not enough to just make and sell cereal. After that you get it half way down the customer's throat through the use of advertising. Then, they've got to swallow it.[7]

Puffed cereal was developed in the early 1920s, and was introduced with great fanfare. The puffing of cereal contributes an added element of treachery to the product. The unnatural puffing process produces chemical changes in the grains that could cause toxicity. Paul Stitt, in his tenure at the Quaker Oats Company, witnessed research data regarding animal feeding experiments with Puffed Wheat.[8] The report detailed an experiment in which four groups of rats were fed special diets. One group received plain whole-wheat kernels, water, and a vitamin and mineral solution. Another group was given water and white sugar. The third group was fed nothing but water and the vitamin and mineral solution, and the fourth group was fed Puffed Wheat, water and the identical vitamin and mineral solution.

The rats eating the whole wheat diet lived more than one year. The rats who received only water and the vitamin and mineral solution lived for about eight weeks. The animals fed white sugar and water lived for one month. Quaker Oats' own lab report showed that the rats fed water, the vitamin and mineral solution and all the Puffed Wheat they could eat died within two weeks. Stitt believes the animals died not from malnutrition, but due to some toxic aspect of the Puffed Wheat itself. He suggests the puffing process gives grain a negative nutritional value. Stitt later performed similar tests and found that rats fed a diet of Puffed Wheat do worse than animals eating nothing at all.[8]

Stitt was so shocked at the results of the Quaker animal study that he shared the information with his colleague, Dr. Walter Clark. Upon reviewing the report, Dr. Clark was so upset that he confronted the president of Quaker Oats, whereupon the president remarked:

> I know people should throw it on brides and grooms at weddings but if they insist on sticking it in their mouth, can I help it? Besides, we made $9 million on the stuff last year.[9]

In July of 1970, the Consumers Subcommittee of the Senate Commerce Committee held hearings to evaluate consumer concerns about certain foods. Mr. Robert Choate, a former food consultant to the White House and the Department of Health, Education and Welfare, gave testimony on the subject of breakfast cereals. Mr. Choate stated that laboratory experiments with animals fed breakfast cereals seemed to indicate "that the rats fed on the cereal boxes had fared better than those fed on the cereals themselves."[10] Is this cereal, or surreal?

Margarine, fats and oils. Another modern wonder-product, margarine, is subject to a considerable degree of molecular manipulation during its manufacture. By exposing vegetable oils to the chemical hydrogen—a process known as *hydrogenation*—a more stable product, margarine, is created. The more stable a product is, the longer its shelf-life. During the hydrogenation process, the molecular form of the oils is changed from the natural *cis* form (a horseshoe- or C-shaped molecule), to the harmful *trans* form (a straight-shaped molecule). The hydrogen molecules which are added to the natural *unsaturated* oils make them more *saturated* (with hydrogen). *Trans* fatty acids are molecules that do not occur anywhere in nature, and have been found to produce many serious health detriments (although there are some discrepancies and inconsistencies reported in the research literature which make this subject rather complex and sometimes hotly debated).

Further marginalizing margarine as a consumable, a typical formula for the product presents a grand chemical feast: diacetyl, isopropyl, stearyl citrates, sodium benzoate, benzoic acid, citric acid, monoglycerides and diglycerides. The margarine versus butter battle has been waged since shortly after WWII, with margarine currently the victor. Many see this as a defeat for the consumer, as butter is viewed by most experts as the better alternative:

> Harvard School of Public Health recently published in a prestigious British medical journal that four servings of white bread, cake or cookies that contain "partially hydrogenated fats" can increase the chances of heart trouble by 67% or, 2½ pats of margarine can increase the chance of heart trouble by 100%.[11]

Lipids, or fats and oils as they are commonly called, are necessary for life. (Fats that are liquid at room temperature are referred to as oils.) These substances are utilized by the body as an energy source, and represent the body's main source of stored energy. Essential fatty acids (EFAs) are a special type of fat required by the body to maintain health. "Essential" means that the body does not self-produce these substances—they must be acquired from the diet. Hydrogenated oils interfere and compete with the assimilation of health-giving EFAs. It has been estimated, in fact, that up to 80% of Americans consume insufficient quantities of EFAs in their diets, partially as the result of consuming too much hydrogenated oil. Some experts believe the introduction of processed oils into the market place has all but eliminated EFAs from the average American's diet.

Foods that typically contain either totally or partially hydrogenated oils are processed foods such as snack foods—cakes, cookies, candies, chips, crackers—and processed foods such as meats, cheeses and fried foods. Many grocery store oils also are hydrogenated, e.g., canola, corn, safflower, sesame and sunflower.

In 1993, leading lipid biochemist Dr. Mary Enig reported in *Nutrition Quarterly* that the consumption of hydrogenated oils and *trans* fats has been linked to a long list of physical maladies, including abnormal sperm production and decreased testosterone levels in men; EFA deficiencies; heart disease; increased levels of LDL (bad) cholesterol; low birth weight infants; low volume/quality of breast milk; prostate disease; and suppressed immune function.[12]

Two books for suggested reading are Dr. Udo Erasmus' 1986/ 1993 classic, *Fats that Heal, Fats that Kill*; and Dr. Michael Murray and Jade Beutler's 1996 book *Understanding Fats and Oils: Your Guide to Healing with Essential Fatty Acids.*

Sugar. *The Truth About Sugar* (©1913); *The Sugar Trust: An Amazing Conspiracy* (©1925); *Sweet and Dangerous* (©1972); *Sugar Blues* (©1975); *Lick the Sugar Habit* (©1996) and *Sugar Busters* (©1998). The names and publication dates of these books suggest the detriments of this white, crystalline substance are well documented and have been known for some time. Introduced by Jesuits who brought sugar cane and cane plants from Haiti to New Orleans around the mid-1700s, these sweet crystals are presently promoted by industry trade associations as "nature's miracle food," and as a perfect source of quick energy, although nothing could be further from the truth.

Most health authorities regard excess intake of refined sugar as a detriment to the body—merely "empty" or "naked" calories. Whereas beet and cane sugars possess the vitamins, minerals and proteins necessary for proper digestion of the substance, refined sugar has been stripped of these vital elements resulting in incomplete carbohydrate metabolism. Brown sugar offers no advantage over its pale counterpart; it can be even more refined. Toxic metabolites are produced which interfere with cellular respiration. The body's cells are starved of oxygen and either die or function abnormally. This has the potential of affecting every organ in the body, resulting in illness and degenerative diseases.

Sugar has been shown to suppress the immune function.[13] In a society plagued by immune disorders, the high level of sugar consumption of most Americans, about ¼ to ⅓ of a pound per day,[14] only adds to the body's burden. As the immune system becomes depressed, the body requires an increased intake of vitamins and minerals, whether from an external source or from the body's own repository.

Sugar is a hidden or unnoticed ingredient in most modern foods, including soft drinks (which contain up to 15 tablespoons);

canned vegetables and fruits; spiced cheeses; ketchup (about 50% sugar); chewing gum (½ teaspoon per stick); and most everything else from soup to nuts. Even cigarettes contain sugar—about 10% in the U.S. product and 17% in British cigarettes.[15] Each year the average American consumes roughly his or her own weight in sugar—about 150 pounds,[16] with non-caloric sweeteners tacking on another 50 pounds or so. Research suggests that people who consume more than four ounces of sugar per day—less than the national average—have a 500% increased risk of suffering a heart attack than those who consume two ounces or less.[17] A single, solitary soda pop can contain as much as two ounces of sweet immune suppression.

Artificial sweeteners. Two hundred times sweeter than sugar—a little goes a long way—the artificial sweetener aspartame is marketed as NutraSweet,® Equal,® Spoonful,® Benevia,® Natra-Taste®and by other trade names. This compound comes with its own unique set of suspicions. Although approved for use as a table-top sweetener in 1981 and in soft drinks in 1983, aspartame has been implicated in causing brain tumors in animals. In humans it has been shown to cause headaches and seizures, and to have adverse effects on the brain development of young children.[18] About 40% of NutraSweet is the amino acid aspartate, which becomes a deadly neurotoxin when consumed over a critical level. Several hours following exposure, nerve cells within the brain and spinal cord (neurons) suddenly die, as if the cells had been excited to death. The term *excitotoxins* has been given to a group of similar-acting toxins including aspartate.

The remaining 60% of NutraSweet is composed of phenyla-lanine (50%) and methyl esters (10%). Phenylalanine has been shown to penetrate the blood-brain barrier with ease, and be transformed into dopamine and dopamine metabolites. Addictive drugs are known to flood synapses (the points at which nerve impulses transfer from one neuron to another) with dopamine. This powerful neurotransmitter carries a pleasure message along the neural pathways, creating a "high." (Cocaine, for example, is a dopamine re-uptake inhibitor, thereby acting as an indirect dopamine antagonist.)

Methyl alcohol (methanol) is another component of aspartame, which is further oxidized by the body into formaldehyde (a deadly neurotoxin, carcinogen and embalming fluid used as a tissue preservative) and formate, or formic acid.[19] Methanol works great as an automobile racing fuel, but is not recommended for use in humans.

Over 75% of all complaints to the FDA are related to aspartame use. More than 10,000 complaints have been filed involving more than 90 symptoms, including addiction, anxiety, blindness, blurred vision, depression, dizziness, fatigue, hearing loss, insomnia, joint pain, nausea, seizures and spasms. Over 100 million Americans consume more than 5,000 tons of aspartate as NutraSweet annually.

The manufacturer of NutraSweet, G.D. Searle & Company (owned by Monsanto/Pharmacia), spent over $60 million on advertising during the sweetener's first three years on the market. Eight years after its introduction, Searle ranked ninth on the list of Fortune 500 companies. In 1988 alone, Searle reaped rewards of $736 million in sales. Two years after FDA Commissioner Arthur Hayes approved aspartame for the U.S. market (after overruling his own board of inquiry), he retired from the FDA to join a G.D. Searle public relation firm. The huge profitability of aspartame makes it difficult for the toxic overseers to find fault with the product—at least until another sweet stellar performer rises in the corporate sky.

More information on the harmful effects of aspartame can be found in Dr. H.J. Roberts' recent book *Aspartame Disease: An Ignored Epidemic*. Also visit www.aspartameispoison.com; or the Mission Possible Web site at www.dorway.com. Dr. Russell Blaylock's classic, *Excitotoxins: The Taste that Kills*, provides further information.

One dim star has risen, in 1998 in the U.S., and Canada in 1991. Most European countries are reserving judgement as no long-term studies have been done to date. Known by its trade name Splenda,® this product may produce less than the splendid results reported by its manufacturer. Created by a molecular manipulation of the sugar molecule—producing a molecule called *sucralose*—Splenda is some 600 times sweeter than sugar. Although its manufacturer states that Splenda is not absorbed by the body, the FDA's "Final Rule" reported that 11-27% of sucralose is absorbed. The jury is still out on the long-term effects of Splenda.

Salt. Sugar's crystalline cousin, salt is another substance that has not escaped the eye of the food giants. Traded by peoples throughout the world since the dawn of civilization, salt has been valued as highly as gold at various times throughout history. The health benefits of salt harvested from the active oceans have long been recognized by man. Sea salt contains all of the broad spectrum of major minerals and trace elements found in sea water, many of which have been stripped from the soil and therefore the food supply.

The mineral content of sea water is similar to the human body's extracellular fluid which constitutes about 20% of the body's fluids. It stands to reason this natural form of salt would be beneficial to the body, unlike its refined counterpart. Today's refined, store-bought salt is very different from the natural sea salt prized by people throughout millennia. Modern salt is roughly 98% pure sodium chloride, with virtually all of the beneficial mineral salts processed out to be sold to industry for the manufacture of chlorine gas, explosives, fertilizers, plastics and soda. This refined version has lost all but two of its minerals, and its ionic and electrolytic properties as well.[20] It is interesting to note that industry consumes over 90% of the refined/processed salt—which is required to be pure sodium chloride. About 8% is used by humans as a condiment.

Many medical authorities believe the intake of modern, refined salt can lead to hypertension (high blood pressure). However, most people are unaware that natural sea salt can be beneficial to the body. Dr. Bruce West, author of the *Health Alert* newsletter (800-944-6465), is a physician who believes sea salt has many positive influences on the body, including the reduction of hypertension. Dr. West comments, "When it comes to heart disease and hypertension...sea salt [is] indispensable. In fact, sea salt serves as a magnesium 'tonic' in these cases." The modification of salt from a beneficial substance to a health detriment is yet another example of an industry losing its way in the dark...green.

Since all salt has its origins in the sea, it is not surprising to find masqueraders in the marketplace calling themselves sea salt, but are not. If the salt is not light grey and moist, chances are it has lost its beneficial minerals to the refining process. Dr. West states there is only one source of real sea salt of which he is aware, Celtic Sea Salt which is available in various health food stores throughout the U.S. Inquiries should be directed to the importers of Celtic salt, the Grain & Salt Society of Asheville, N.C.; (800) TOP SALT.

The following are some additional facts about processed foods:

♦ According to the United States FDA, about 1 billion pounds of chemical additives are used in foods each year, with each person consuming more than 50 pounds annually.[21]

♦ The Center for Science in the Public Interest reported that the only difference between General Mills' Wheaties® and Total® breakfast cereals is that 1.5¢ of synthetic vitamins are sprayed on Total, which is then sold for 65¢ more than Wheaties—a practice that generated $425 million in additional profits for General Mills from 1972-1990.[22]

♦ The Nabisco Company spent millions of dollars developing the formulation for Oreo® cookies, so that you can't eat just one. Oreos contain 23 different appetite stimulants and 11 artificial colors.[23]

♦ There are many foods that have no labeling requirement. Breads, for example, can contain up to 80 unlisted ingredients, including oxides of nitrogen, chlorine, nitrosyl chloride, chlorine dioxide, benzoyl peroxide (the active ingredient in a famous acne medication), acetone peroxide, azodicarbonamide, and plaster of Paris.[24] In fact, there are over 300 foods such as ice cream, ketchup and mayonnaise, that require absolutely no labeling whatsoever.

♦ More than 20 varieties of fruits and vegetables are being coated with wax to extend shelf-life. Various waxes are obtained from plants, petrochemicals, insects and other animals. Some imported foods are coated with beef tallow. Often, pesticides and fungicides are added to the waxes.[25]

♦ The canning process reduces much of the nutrient content of most foods, with the reduction of most vitamins and minerals ranging from 20-75%.[26]

♦ Most infant milk formulas contain only 20% of the essential fat of breast milk.[27]

♦ Methylene chloride, the most widely-used solvent for extracting caffeine from coffee beans, is a proven liver and lung cancer promoter in animals. Manufacturers claim the solvent evaporates during manufacture, yet some researchers believe an uncertain amount of toxic chemical residue remains.[28]

♦ Americans consume over 30 pounds per person of hydrogenated vegetable oils (*trans* fats) each year in the form of margarines, cooking oils, and shortenings.[29]

♦ Over 1,600 chemical additives not requiring labeling disclosure are permitted to be used in ice cream manufacture,[30] some of which are distinctly unpalatable. For example the additive piperonal, used as a vanilla substitute, is also used as a lice-killing agent. Butyraldehyde imparts a nutty flavor to ice creams, but also multi-tasks as an ingredient in rubber cement. Isoamyl acetate is another dual-purpose ingredient, serving equally well in both confections and shoe polish.[31]

♦ The long-term effects of the following fat substitutes are totally unknown: Olestra® (Proctor & Gamble), Simplesse® (Monsanto), Caprenin® (Proctor & Gamble), and Trailblazer (Kraft General Foods). According to the June 11, 1998 *New York Times* article entitled "Fat Substitute May Cause Disease," top Harvard researchers Walter Willett, M.D. and Meir Stampfer, M.D., suggest that the use of Olestera may cause thousands of additional cases of cancer and heart disease. This significant increase in disease, the researchers believe, would be related to Olestra's interfering with the absorption of fat-soluble vitamins and carotenoids.)

♦ A 1995 report by the Federation for Experimental Biology (FASEB) stated that monosodium glutamate (MSG), an excitotoxin, causes destructive brain lesions and a reduction in endocrine organ weights in all species studied. Motor disturbances, seizure threshold and changes in brain chemistry have also been observed.[32]

♦ Various gases are used to extend the shelf-life of fruits such as bananas, oranges and lemons. These techniques are also applied to some vegetables. Tomatoes, for example, have been kept "fresh" for as long as four years.[33]

♦ The high-temperature pasteurization of milk generates harmful *trans* fats; the homogenization of milk increases the incidence of atherosclerosis.[34]

♦ Collectively, Americans eat 90 acres of pizza per day.[35]

♦ Fifty percent of adult Americans regularly eat frozen, packaged or take-out meals for dinner.[36]

♦ On the average, each American in a given year eats 1,300 pounds of food, including 112 lb. of red meat; 63 lb. of poultry; 15 lb. of seafood; 234 lb. of milk and cream; 236 eggs; 147 lb. of sugar; 60 lb. of cakes, cookies and chocolate; 68 lb. of fats and oils; and 47 gallons of soft drinks.[37]

The list of processed foods goes on and on, with literally thousands upon thousands of entries and entrees—each food competing with the others for shelf space and profit margins, each food chemically tweaked to provide that special "can't eat just one" taste. The food producers have proved most people will eat just about anything. Next time you visit your local supermarket, close your eyes, turn round-and-round, point your finger straight ahead, open your eyes, and you'll probably be pointing at some gourmet delight that could contribute to your ill health. Modern foods truly are a curse of convenience. Quick 'n' Easy, Heat & Serve, Ready-In-A-Jiffy, Boil-In-The-Bag. Our psyches have adapted to these conveniences, but our bodies never will.

Chapter Five

ADDITIVES

Intentional Additives

Additives, as defined by the FDA, are substances other than the basic foods themselves which are present in food as the intentional result of manufacture, production, packaging, preparation, treatment, transportation, irradiation or storage. These chemical substances are added to foods for a variety of purposes, including extending shelf-life with preservatives; making foods more palatable by enhancing or masking flavors; making foods more attractive by modifying the texture and/or color; facilitating processing, and the like. The overall goal, bottom line, is the creation of profit. Issues of health and safety rank a distant second place.

Some people claim "you are what you eat." Others believe "you are what you don't excrete." If either is the case, Americans are fast becoming preserved and chemicalized. American morticians, in fact, have reported that some corpses are taking longer to decay than in times past—an unusual way to attempt immortality.

In 1955, 419 million pounds of chemical additives were used in foods. Today, the number has soared to over one billion pounds, with each American consuming more than 50 pounds of chemical additives per year.[1] In 1958, there were only about 700 chemicals commonly used in foods. There are presently 10,000 food additives being used in the U.S.,[2] many with names such as butyl anthranilate, 1-(p-methoxyphenyl)-1-penten-3-one, and 2-3 (3-phenylpropyl) tetrahydrofuran. (These are synthetic chemicals used in beverages, ice cream, ices and candy—just like grandma used to make.) No toxicity studies have been performed on roughly 45% of these thousands of additives, while only 5% have been thoroughly evaluated.[3] Toxicity data is either inadequate or nonexistent for 80% of all additives.[4] Since 1972, more than 30 additives have been banned from use due to a demonstrated association with either toxicity or cancer.

Food additives are potentially dangerous in several ways. Some additives produce chemical changes within the food itself, thus altering the food's biological structure. Other additives may form toxic compounds when interacting with substances present within the food. The synergy of additives also poses a threat as potentially toxic chemicals interact within the body with each other and with hundreds of thousands of other substances such as pesticide residues, alcohol, tobacco and prescription drugs, to name only a few. It is virtually impossible to understand the interplay between the 10,000 food additives in use today, and the more than 70,000 other chemical substances used throughout society (only 2% of which have been tested for toxicity),[5] with another 700 new chemicals entering the market every year.[6]

In 1976, The Journal of Food Science reported an experiment that demonstrates the problem of synergistic interactions of chemicals. Three different chemicals were tested one at a time on rats—no effect was noted. When two chemicals were simultaneously added, the rats became ill. When three chemicals were added in combination, all of the animals died within two weeks.[7]

In 1969, Dr. Irving Selikoff, professor of environmental medicine at Mount Sinai School of Medicine, made a prophetic statement while being interviewed on NBC television:

> We may eventually see diseases that we don't even begin to understand at this time. Also, the sum total of these various low-level contaminants—each in itself not very important—may be to generally shorten life [due to the] total body burden of environmental contaminants.[8]

Unintentional Additives

In addition to chemicals purposely added to foods, there are substances which unintentionally become part of the food supply. These substances include pesticides, drug residues, food-borne pathogens and physical contaminants.

Pesticides. Pesticides are a group of chemicals that include insecticides, herbicides and fungicides. More than three billion pounds per year of 50,000 pesticidal chemicals generate more than $10 billion in annual sales for their U.S. manufacturers.[9] The problem with pesticides, i.e., killers of pests, is that they are poisonous, and at least some of the poisons leave residues both on the outside of the food item (in the case of produce), as well as interwoven within the matrix of both plants and meats. Although some of the residue can be washed off the exterior of plants, some chemical molecules of the pesticides are inexorably bound into the cellular structure of both plants and meats.[10] In some instances, the chemical is present only within the plant's structure, while none is detectable on the plant's surface.

The various watch-dog agencies of the government claim the low levels of pesticides that may be present on or within food stuffs are insufficient to be of any harm to consumers. Modern science recognizes this assumption to be questionable at best. It is well known that certain substances are active within the body at exceedingly low levels, in the ranges of parts per million (ppm), parts per billion (ppb) or parts per trillion (ppt). To clarify how small these levels actually are, one ppm is equal to approximately one drop in 16 gallons; one ppb is approximately equal to one drop in 16,000 gallons; and one part per trillion is equal to approximately one drop in 16,000,000 gallons. To help you better wrap your head around the concept of a "trillion," here is an example: If you began counting to one trillion and counted a new number every second, it would take you 32,000 years to finish your count. You can see that one part in a trillion is very small indeed. Yet, it has been shown that certain substances ingested into the body in these minute dosages can have significant, harmful results.

During the 1950s, many pesticide manufacturers advertised with the slogan "harmless to humans, but deadly to all bugs." Catchy phrase, but dead wrong. The toxicity of pesticides is exemplified by the world's worst industrial accident which occurred several years ago at an insecticide manufacturing plant in Bhopal, India. Seepage of the insecticide methyl isocyanate killed 2,000 people overnight, 3,500 total, and 200,000 more were maimed.[11] This severe effect on human life occurred at the hands of a chemical that was intended to be sprayed on food to be consumed by both animals and humans.

Another example of the toxicity of pesticidal chemicals is the infamous, patented German insecticide Zyklon-B, which produced the hydrogen cyanide gas used at German WWII concentration camps from 1939 to 1945. Phosgene, developed as a chemical warfare weapon and used in WWI, is used today to produce pesticides.[12]

The EPA classifies the following pesticides presently in use as probable carcinogens: Captan, Daminozide, Mancozeb, Mevinphos, Parathion and Quintozene, to name only a few. One of the difficulties in evaluating the toxicity of such chemicals is that there can be a latency period of up to 20 years from the time of exposure until symptoms and illness manifest. Despite massive evidence to the contrary, some government agencies and chemical manufacturers continue to claim no threat is posed to the public from the small quantities of pesticide residues present on and in today's foodstuffs. It is unfortunate the public has to take any risk at all in connection with the food supply. According to a National Academy of Sciences report published in 1984, 30% of all insecticides, 60% of all herbicides and 90% of all fungicides are carcinogenic.[13]

There are three principal types of synthetic pesticides: 1) Organochlorines (e.g., DDT, Agent Orange, chlordane and heptachlor), 2) Organophosphates (e.g., malathion and parathion), and 3) Carbamates (e.g., carbaryl and carbofuran). One of the first pesticides to gain public awareness was DDT (dichloro diphenyl trichloroethane), a man-made molecule of organic synthesis that does not degrade in nature, and can exist in both soil and water at full toxicity for hundreds if not thousands of years. DDT was invented in 1948 by the Swiss chemist Paul Müller, for which he was dubiously awarded a Nobel Prize. Although DDT was banned during the late 1960s as the result of massive public protest relating to its carcinogenicity, the chemical is still found in seals in the Arctic Ocean, penguins and seals in Antarctica and in frogs living at very high altitudes in the Sierra Nevada mountains in the U.S.[14]

Interestingly, even at the time of the chemical's banning, the USDA was still claiming that such chemicals were used "under federal controls deigned to keep foods free of unsafe, high-level chemical residues."[15] DDT was and is a money maker. It continues to be produced and sold to Third World countries such as Mexico, from which we import over half of all our vegetables. Additionally, half of all U.S. winter produce is imported, and is twice as likely as domestic produce to be contaminated by illegal pesticides.[16]

The pesticide dieldrin, 40 times more poisonous than DDT when absorbed through the skin, was banned in 1974. This chemical is one of the most potent carcinogens known to man, producing cancer in laboratory animals even in the most infinitesimal concentrations. Before dieldren was banned, the FDA reported it was found in 96% of all meats, fish and poultry; 85% of all dairy products; and in the tissues of all U.S. residents.[17] Because dieldren is one of the most biologically stable pesticides, it will remain toxic for decades if not centuries. Although it is no longer in use, for years dieldren was applied to land presently used to grow barley, corn, oats, soy and alfalfa used to feed livestock[18]—which is then consumed by humans.

Heptachlor is another pesticide that has come under scrutiny for many years. According to the Environmental Defense Fund of Washington, D.C., meat, fish, poultry and dairy products in the U.S. are highly contaminated with this chemical. Author John Robbins, in his best-selling book *Diet for a New America*, comments:

> In November, 1974, the EPA finally began hearings and appeals to determine if the chemical [heptachlor] should be banned. But heptachlor was such a huge money-maker for Velsicol Chemical Corporation that the company spent literally tens of millions of dollars on legal maneuvers to fight a possible ban at every step of the way. The company's tactics included withholding lab reports from the EPA which showed malignant tumors had been produced in animals exposed to heptachlor. When this "accidental oversight" was discovered, several company officials were indicted by a federal grand jury.[19]

Dioxin is an herbicide that was an ingredient of Agent Orange, a chemical sprayed over the jungles of Vietnam as a defoliant. Agent Orange gained notoriety for having caused many physical ailments in Vietnam veterans, including immune disorders, miscarriages, stillbirths and birth defects. Vietnamese women living in Da Nang still have breast milk dioxin levels 75% higher than American women.[20] In 1974, Dr. Diane Courtney of the EPA described dioxin as "by far the most toxic chemical known to man."[21] One drop of dioxin can kill 1,000 people; an ounce can kill one million people.[22] It has been shown to cause cancer, birth defects, miscarriages and death in laboratory animals in concentrations as low as one part per trillion.[23] Agent Orange's two active ingredients, 2,4-D and 2,4,5-T, are currently in use today on acreage used to grow food for livestock such as cattle, swine and poultry.[24] 2,4,5-T contains dioxin. According to the EPA, cattle and dairy products contain dioxin as the result of grazing on treated land. The chemical, as with so many other pesticides, accumulates in the fatty tissues of animals, including man. Dow Chemical, the manufacturer of 2,4,5-T, claims that the chemical "is about as toxic as aspirin."[25] In an appearance on NBC's *Today* show, then president Paul Oreffice (no pun intended) of Dow told the audience that "there's absolutely no evidence of dioxin doing any damage to humans."[26] Others think differently. Says John Robbins:

> Because the chlorinated hydrocarbon pesticides have such an extremely poisonous and persistent nature, environmentally aware people have urged and pleaded and demanded and begged that this entire chemical family be outlawed. But the very poisonous and persistent qualities of these toxic chemicals have made them big moneymakers for the chemical companies who market them aggressively. These corporations have applied enormous political and economic pressure to keep their products in use. The tragic result is that millions of pounds of these lethal agents continue to be used every year.[27]

Keptone is an extremely toxic pesticide known to cause cancer, birth defects and neurological disorders. During the 1970s, Life Sciences, Inc., a subsidiary of Allied Chemical Corporation, dumped huge quantities of keptone into the James River in Virginia, once the seabed for roughly 25% of the oysters harvested in the U.S.[28] The keptone spread into the Chesapeake Bay, which produced about 90% of America's softshell crabs, 40% of the commercial oysters, 15% of the softshell clams, as well as a sizable portion of America's commercial fishing harvest.[29] Experts say that the keptone contamination site will remain toxic for another 200 years. When Allied Chemical's dumping practice was discovered, a Senate Committee was established to investigate the matter. Chairman of the committee, Senator Patrick Lahey, commented on the public posture assumed by Allied Chemical, stating that "Allied Chemical took a position that makes Pontius Pilate look like Mother Theresa of Calcutta. That is giving them the benefit of the doubt."[30]

The following are some additional facts about pesticides:

♦ According to a report published in the *American Journal of Public Health*, women who live in California farming counties have a 190% higher incidence of significant birth defects than California women living in non-farming counties.[31]

♦ Since pesticides are fat-soluble, most of their residues are stored in high-fat foods such as milk.[32] Cow's milk containing a pesticide at a concentration of 2 parts per million (ppm) may produce butter containing up to 25 ppm.

♦ According to the National Academy of Sciences, over 70% of all pesticides sold in the U.S. have not been properly tested for cancer-causing effects.[33]

♦ According to the USDA, no "commercial" milk available in any part of the U.S. is free from chemical pesticide residues.[34]

♦ Less than 1% of domestic and imported foods are inspected for pesticide contamination.[35]

♦ According to a 1969 article published in the *Annals of the New York Academy of Sciences*, all children born in the U.S. at that time had traces of pesticides in their tissues.[36]

♦ Ninety percent of American children under the age of five are presently exposed to at least 13 toxic insecticides in their baby foods.[37]

♦ According to the *Pesticides Monitoring Journal*, more than 90% of all pesticides present in foods comes from meats, fish, dairy products and eggs.[38]

♦ According to the National Cancer Institute, the active ingredient in 1,500 pesticides, 2,4-D, is carcinogenic to humans.[39] This chemical is used in both commercial agriculture as well as home gardening.

♦ Over the last 50 years, male sperm counts have dropped 50% worldwide. About 20% of American males were considered functionally sterile as of 1980. These infertile males were shown to have higher than average pesticide levels in their semen.[40]

♦ Since the 1972 banning of DDT, there has been no overall decrease of DDT levels in human breast milk.[41]

♦ Benzene hexachloride, commonly found in butter, hotdogs and milk chocolate, is a pesticide 19 times as potent as DDT.[42]

♦ Due to the intra-cellular uptake of pesticides within plants, washing, rinsing or peeling may remove only some external residue.[43] In 1994, the USDA reported systemic pesticides were found in 61% of washed and peeled samples of produce.[44]

♦ The EPA ranks pesticide contamination as the number three cancer risk, behind cigarette smoking and radon gas.[45] In reality, the sequence of these high risk contaminants could prove to be in reverse order.

♦ The synergistic effects of thousands of chemical pesticides are totally unknown. Over 50,000 different pesticide products are currently in use today.[46]

Fertilizers. Before discussing the problems associated with the use of agricultural fertilizers, a brief discussion about the nature of soil is in order. An ancient Chinese proverb states, "The strength of a nation depends on the strength of her topsoil." In a more recent insight Boyd Gibbons, writing in *National Geographic* magazine, makes the following observations:

> How readily we manipulate our soil. We rearrange and restructure it. We pump it full of chemicals, we flood it, we drain it. On its health the fate of empires has rested...In our cities, rivers of concrete keep us from its touch...But a close look reveals that the soil is an essential bridge between the rock below and the life above.[47]

Others have noted the importance of the soil which grows our food crops. Dr. Alexis Carrel, 1912 Nobel Laureate in Medicine, had this understanding of the nature of soil:

> Soil is the basis of all human life and our only hope for a healthy
> world...All life will be either healthy or unhealthy according to the
> fertility of the soil. Minerals in the soil control the metabolism of
> cells in plants and animals and man...Diseases are created chiefly by
> destroying the harmony reigning among mineral substances present
> in infinitesimal amounts in the air, water and food, but most impor-
> tantly in the soil.[48]

Unfortunately, civilized man has not demonstrated good stew-
ardship of the land. Throughout most of the modern world, the
topsoil that grows the food crops is severely nutrient deficient.
Those vital nutrients that fuel man's bodies—especially the minerals—are no longer present in sufficient quantities in the soil that
grows the crops we eat and depend upon for our good health and
prosperity. The fruits, vegetables, grains and other food plants we
consume today contain a mere shadow of their nutritional content in comparison to several hundred years ago, even 100 years
ago.

When the early pioneers and farmers traveled westward, often in search of more productive, less depleted soils, they discovered some of the richest, most fertile land on earth. The topsoil
was black, rich and thick, and produced exceedingly nutrient-rich
food crops. However, as the early settlers began to farm this land,
especially on a more intensive level than mere subsistence farming, they discovered that within a few short years their lands would
no longer produce the abundant crops they once had. The problem was that their food crops were stripping the soil of the vital
nutrients necessary to sustain a healthful life.

In 1936, the United States Senate studied the issue of soil
nutrient depletion. Published by the 2nd Session of the 74th Congress, Document No. 264 is revealing testimony given before the
Senate. Included in the testimony is the following:

> Do you know that most of us today are suffering from certain dan-
> gerous diet deficiencies which cannot be remedied until the depleted
> soils from which our foods come are brought into proper mineral
> balance? The alarming fact is that foods—fruits and vegetables and

grains—now being raised on millions of acres of land that no longer contain enough of certain needed minerals, are starving us—no matter how much of them we eat!...

Laboratory tests prove that the fruits, the vegetables, the grains, the eggs, and even the milk and the meats of today are not what they were a few generations ago. (Which doubtless explains why our forefathers thrived on a selection of food that would starve us!)...No man of today can eat enough fruits and vegetables to supply his system with the mineral salts he requires for perfect health, because his stomach isn't big enough to hold them!...

It is bad news to learn from our leading authorities that 99% of the American people are deficient in these minerals, and a marked deficiency in any one of the more important minerals actually results in disease. Any upset of the balance, any considerable lack of one or another element, however microscopic the body requirement may be, and we sicken, suffer and shorten our lives. This discovery is one of the latest and most important contributions of science to the problem of human health...

Lacking vitamins, the system can make some use of minerals, but lacking minerals, vitamins are useless...Certainly our well-being is more directly dependent on the minerals we take into our systems than upon calories or vitamins or upon the precise proportions of starch, protein or carbohydrates we consume...

So it goes, down through the list, each mineral element playing a definite role in nutrition. A characteristic set of symptoms, just as specific as any vitamin-deficiency disease, follows a deficiency in any one of them. It is alarming, therefore, to face the fact that we are starving for these health-giving substances.[49]

In the time since the 1936 Senate report was published, none of our modern farming techniques has been able to restore the mineral content of the farmlands. On the contrary, the nutrient content of the soil continues to decrease at an accelerated rate as the direct result of factors such as acid rain; animal grazing; deforestation and mining (wherein plant roots literally mine the minerals from the soil); and chemical pesticides and fertilizers.

Fifty years ago, for example, spinach contained about 80 milligrams of iron per 100 grams, as produced by our best farmlands. By 1965, the content had dropped to about 30 mg of iron. Today, spinach barely contains 2 mg of iron per 100 grams. This means that one would have to eat more than 40 times the amount of spinach to receive the same amount of iron compared to about 50 years ago. Woe is Popeye!

In June of 1992, the *Earth Summit Report* was issued from Rio de Janeiro, Brazil. This startling report documents the continued decline in the mineral content of the continents of Earth (% = percentage of depleted minerals over the past 100 years): Australia—55%, Europe—72%, Africa—74%, Asia—76%, South America—76%, and North America—85%.

Today, the topsoil loss in the United States is estimated at seven billion tons annually. The Earth loses about seven percent of its topsoil every 10 years, and it can take 5,000 years to produce five new inches. Two hundred years ago, most of America's crop lands had at least 21 inches of topsoil. Presently, most crop lands have six inches or less, and the loss is accelerating. The remaining soil is severely nutrient deficient and is not able to produce food crops that contain a broad spectrum of vital nutrients.

One might wonder why the appropriate governmental agencies haven't concerned themselves with the issue of reconstituting the soil to its once mineral-rich state. In a 1991 policy statement published in the Federal Register, the U.S. Food and Drug Administration stated that the soil of our farmlands is *not* depleted in any way, nor is the food produced by modern agricultural methods in any way nutrient deficient. In light of thousands of years of farming experience, as well as incontrovertible evidence to the contrary put forth by a multiplicity of expert sources (not to mention Senate Document No. 264, the information disclosed in the 1992 *Earth Summit Report* and a significant amount of the USDA's own data), is the FDA's 1991 policy statement an example of forgotten knowledge and understanding, a simple oversight on their part, or other concerns?

Fertilizers are but one of the many factors contributing to the degradation of the soil. Many of these chemicals destroy the tiny fungal, protozoan, bacterial and other microorganisms which live in the soil and perform many important functions. One tea-spoon of healthy, non-chemically-treated farming soil is host to hundreds of thousands of living organisms. These microorganisms help plants convert inorganic minerals into a form they are able to absorb through their root systems. They also help maintain the proper balance and proportion of minerals absorbed by the plants' roots. Without the presence of these microorganisms, the soil and its resulting crops are severely deficient and weakened.

Industrial fertilizers were introduced in the U.S. during the early 1900s and have been used in similar formulations to the present day. As the chemical industries grew, their involvement in agriculture followed suit. The conclusion of WWII found the U.S. munitions industry with huge, unused inventories of nitrates and nitrogen, the principal ingredients of bombs and explosive shells. Directly following the war, these surplus chemicals found their way into chemical fertilizers in the form of the fertilizer type known as NPK:[50] (N) Nitrogen, (P) Phosphorous and (K) Potassium (nitrate). NPK fertilizer is the type that has been used in U.S. farming since around 1900, and although it serves as one of the pillars of modern agriculture, the rational behind its use points in the direction of economics rather than the production of high-quality, nutritious foods.

The use of NPK fertilizer produces a maximum yield of visu-ally attractive crops, but does not restore many of the natural mineral elements required in human nutrition. Dozens of other minerals also required by the body are not replaced, and the soil continues to produce crops lacking in many of the nutrients es-sential for the prevention of illness and disease. Consequently, although people of modern cultures have available a plentiful va-riety of produce, its nutritive value is sorely lacking.

On an historical note, the renowned German chemist Baron Justice von Liebig initially formulated the NPK theory of crop nourishment in the 1840s. He reasoned that plants need only these three minerals to achieve all of their optimal properties, and that they could be force-fed this "artificial manure," as it was called, to grow crops which meet the nutritional requirements of healthy humans. Based on von Liebig's ideas, the German chemical agricultural industry flourished, and his NPK formulation was soon in use world wide.

Many years later, von Liebig himself realized the error he had made in proposing this method of unnatural crop nourishment. Toward the end of his life, he expressed deep remorse for having offered this misguided contribution to the agricultural industry. His remorseful hindsights are recorded in the 1899 edition of *The Encyclopedia Britannica*. Needless to say, because of the tremendous monetary rewards reaped by the chemical agricultural industry around the world, his remorseful comments have fallen on deaf ears for nearly a century and a half.

Several soil-building techniques presently exist that can adequately accomplish the task of reconstituting the soil of our farmlands to their former mineral-rich state. One of the most capable of these methods is remineralization through the application of finely-ground rock powder known as *rock flour* or *stone meal*. The technique was developed in Germany as early as the 1890s, although it is likely that only a handful of American farmers are familiar with the method. The benefit of rock dust lies in the plants' ability to convert raw-rock minerals into the organic, bioavailable form required by the human body. The countries of Australia and Switzerland have small industries promoting the use of rock dust.

Further complicating the issue of chemical fertilizers, in July of 1997 *The Seattle Times*[51] ran a series of articles exposing a dangerous practice of the U.S. fertilizer industry—a practice that is little known even though it has been part of the industry for several decades. In an effort to find an inexpensive means of disposing the industrial chemical byproducts of manufacture, i.e., chemical waste, several heavy manufacturing industries such as metal (aluminum and steel), cement, paper and wood product companies have been recycling their waste as an ingredient of fertilizer—the same fertilizer that is spread over farmlands and family gardens throughout the U.S. This industrial waste is laden with heavy metals and other dangerous materials such as aluminum, arsenic, beryllium, cadmium, dioxins, lead, mercury, radionuclides and titanium. Some of the ingredients contained within these brews of chemical waste would be beneficial to crop growth if it weren't for the high levels of other toxic substances they contain.

The practice of selling industrial waste as fertilizer is legal within the U.S., and for decades has had the approval of the EPA, the government agency tasked to oversee toxic waste disposal. According to the EPA, only agriculturally-beneficial chemicals need be listed as ingredients of fertilizer products; harmful ingredients such as toxic metals and other dangerous pollutants require no listing. In the U.S., any material that has fertilizing qualities can be labeled and used as plant fertilizer regardless of any other dangerous or potentially dangerous material(s) it contains. What was once a toxic waste product of industry becomes a fertilizer merely by changing the materials' description. President Dick Camp of Bay Zinc, one company that recycles waste to farmers, told *The Seattle Times:*

> When it goes into our silo, it's a hazardous waste...When it comes out of the silo, it's no longer regulated. The exact same material. Don't ask me why. That's the wisdom of the EPA.[52]

The following are some specific examples of recycled waste currently being practiced or under consideration: [53]

- ♦ Low-level radioactive waste from the Sequoyal Fuels Uranium Processing facility in Oklahoma is being sprayed on 9,000 acres of animal grazing land—after which humans consume the animals or animal byproducts. The material is called Raffinate and is registered as a fertilizer with the Oklahoma Department of Agriculture.

- ♦ In Deer Trail, Colorado a proposal has been made to recycle contents from one of the country's worst Superfund landfills containing solvents, petroleum oils, pesticides and radioactive materials. The material would be treated with sewage treatment techniques and then applied to a 50,000 acre government-owned wheat farm.

♦ Seven hundred tons per month of highly corrosive ash laced with heavy metals is collected from the chimney of a giant pulp and paper mill in Camas, Washington. The ash is classified as a dangerous waste by the state of Washington, but this exact material is used as a fertilizer called Nutri-Lime,® registered for farm use in Washington and Oregon. NutriLime is used to grow oats, clover, grass and other crops for livestock consumption.

Dr. Bill Liebhardt, chairman of the Sustainable Agriculture Department at the University of California-Davis campus told *The Times*:

> Even if it's legal, to me it's just morally and ethically bankrupt that you would take this toxic material and mix it into something that is beneficial and then sell that to unsuspecting people. To me, it's just outrageous."[54]

Chemist Edward Kleppinger, who during the 1970s wrote hazardous waste regulations for the EPA, commented:

> The heavy metals don't disappear...They're not biodegradable. They just use this as an alternate way to get rid of hazardous waste, this whole recycling loophole that EPA has left in place these last 20 years...The last refuge of the hazardous-waste scoundrel is to call it a fertilizer or soil amendment and dump it on farmland.[55]

There seems to be a consensus among scientists that toxic chemicals placed on the land can become part of the internal structure of the plants grown in chemical-laden soils. If this is true, eating the plants or the animals that eat the plants, would pose a significant health hazard. However, experts at the USDA have assured consumers there is little reason for concern. They say the dangerous chemicals are highly unlikely to move through the food chain to humans. That's good news for consumers—a relief. How do you spell relief? In this case: POISON.

Canada's head fertilizer regulator, Darlene Blair, told *The Times*:

> They're congratulating people for recycling things without understanding what the problems are with the recycled material...We're a little bit beyond the point where we wait till something is proved bad before we fix it. Sorry, but we won't compromise our health.[56]

Mrs. Blair's comments seem obvious enough. Does it take a rocket scientist, or in this instance a soil scientist, to figure out what would seem blatantly obvious to a 5th grader, a 2nd grader even? The governments of Canada, Australia, New Zealand and most of the European Community have figured it out, and do not allow such contaminating practices for the sole sake of big business, to the detriment of the good health of their citizens.

Pharmaceutical Drugs. In 1986, a House Government Operations subcommittee studied the problem of drug-residue-contaminated human foods. Among its conclusions, the subcommittee reported that the FDA is failing to perform its duty of protecting the food supply from harmful drug residues by allowing the food producers to use thousands of unapproved pharmaceuticals on animals intended for market.[57] These drugs are used either as animal medications or as aids to increase animal production. Residues of these drugs can be present in meat, eggs and animal byproducts such as cheese, milk and the like.

Pigs, for example, are injected with tranquilizers immediately before transport to slaughter. The full pharmacological action of the drug is still in effect at the moment of slaughter. Also, a variety of veterinary drugs are used to treat animals. These drugs may be present within the animals' tissues at the time of slaughter. Long-lasting implantable or injectable drugs such as hormones may also be present in the animals' tissues at the time of slaughter.

Hormones. Hormones are potent chemical substances secreted by the body to control certain bodily functions. The use of hormones in livestock production first occurred following WWII. Manufacturers of the first synthetic hormone, diethylstilbestrol, or DES, called the chemical a miracle and hailed its introduction as "the most important moment in the history of food production"[58] due to its ability to substantially increase the weight, hence profit, of the animal. The farmers who used DES quickly discovered their miracle drug had undesirable human medical consequences such as impotence, infertility and changes in their vocal register. Only after tons of DES were given to animals being fattened for market was it also discovered that DES causes cancer even in infinitesimal amounts as low as one ten-thousandth of an ounce. The hormone was then banned from use, although some factory farms may continue to use DES illegally.[59] Other similar hormones were soon to take the place of DES, many of which contain the same or similar constituent ingredients. Steer-oid® and Compu-dose® are two such hormones used in most commercial feedlot (cattle farming) operations.[60]

Various other hormones are used in animal production to increase the growth rate and fatten the animal—more product in a shorter amount of time, and more money in the producers' coffers. Testosterone, estradiol, progesterone and the two synthetic hormones zeranol and trenbolone acetate are also used in cattle production. By using these hormones, a head of cattle will increase by 200-300 pounds at slaughter, although there is an accompanying increase in tissue estrogen content of about 35%.[61]

One of the ill effects of using hormones in food production is the epidemic of premature sexual development of consumers as the result of a modification of the body's endocrine system. This is occurring in several countries around the world where the use of hormones is permitted, including the U.S. Children who consume hormone-treated foods are reaching puberty at increasingly earlier ages. Also, increasingly large numbers of children are developing sexual characteristics such as abnormal breast growth (even in males), pubic hair, and an increasing variety of aberrational sexual characteristics.[62]

One of the latest controversies surrounds the use of bovine growth hormone (rBGH, bovine somatotropin) to increase the milk production of cattle. Since 1985 the FDA has allowed the sale of milk containing BGH without disclosing the presence of the hormone. Not uncharacteristically, the FDA claims that milk produced from cattle injected with BGH is safe for human use, although no long-term studies have been done. Currently, approximately 70% of all cattle in the U.S. are receiving BGH injections.[63]

This country has long experienced a milk surplus which is subsidized by the government. At times, millions of dollars have been spent to slaughter cows to reduce this surplus. Does it make sense, in light of these circumstances, that chemicals such as BGH are being used to increase milk production? It has been reported that four companies invested over $1 billion to develop BGH:[64] American Cyanamid, Eli Lilly, Monsanto and Upjohn. Perhaps these companies require a decade or two of sales to recover their investments. It is of interest that the FDA official who approved the use of BGH without the requirement of disclosure was a former Monsanto attorney.[65]

Scientists and consumer groups have pointed out possible dangerous effects of BGH. The presence of BGH in the cow's bloodstream stimulates the production of another hormone, Insulin-like Growth Factor 1, or IGF-1. IGF-1 in cattle is chemially identical to IGF-1 in humans.[66] This hormone causes cells to divide. The question of concern is whether its increased presence within humans will cause an increase in cell division leading to tumor growth. Although more research is needed, one recent study suggests the consumption of milk treated with BGH may increase the risk of cancer in humans.[67]

Antibiotics. As in the case of hormones, antibiotics are also used as an inexpensive means of increasing the growth rate and size of factory-farmed animals. No one knows exactly why these drugs support animal growth, but they have been used for this purpose since 1950.[68] Additionally, the shelf-life of meat, poultry, eggs and dairy products such as milk is extended through the use of antibiotics. Some of the products presently in use include bacitracin, bambemycin, chlortetracycline, erythromycin, lincomycin, monensin, oleandomycin, oxytetracycline, penicillin, tylosin and virginiamycin. Animals receiving antibiotics include catfish, cattle, chicken, lobster, salmon, swine and turkey.[69] At least one antibiotic, chlortetracycline, is used to retard spoilage of fish, poultry, scallops and shrimp. Factory farms presently use approximately 40-50% of the total U.S. antibiotic production primarily to increase animal growth rate, but also to treat and prevent infection.[70]

Antibiotics, as the name implies (anti: against; bios: life), are chemical agents that destroy or inhibit the growth of bacteria and other potentially harmful microorganisms such as parasites (including protozoans and amoebas). Pharmaceutical antibiotics have saved untold thousands of lives since their widespread introduction during WWII. However, there is an ever-increasing danger related to their use, namely, the many antibiotic-resistant strains of microorganisms which began to develop almost as immediately as the drugs were introduced. These resistant microbes, dubbed "super bugs," pose a more significant threat to health than their predecessors in that they are more difficult to destroy.

When harmful microorganisms are treated with an antibiotic, most of the organisms die. However, if any microbes survive treatment, they can pass on resistant genes to their offspring who thus inherit the ability to resist further treatment by that specific antibiotic. (A single surviving bacterium can produce over 16 million offspring within 24 hours.[71]) Furthermore, the mutant survivors are able to share their genetically-resistant DNA with other, unrelated microbes. For example, the bacterium responsible for cholera developed a tetracycline resistance which it acquired from ordinary *E. coli* in the human intestinal tract.[72] Also, some microbes seem to demonstrate a strategic anticipation of new drug treatments, and thus become resistant to drugs they have never previously encountered. In his book *The Antibiotic Paradox: How Miracle Drugs Are Destroying the Miracle*, Dr. Stuart Levy of Tufts University states that "antibiotic usage has stimulated evolutionary changes [in microbes] unparalleled in recorded biologic history."[73]

Just five years after the widespread use of penicillin began during the 1940s, resistant strains of the staphylococcus bacteria were discovered. Although it is a largely unknown fact outside the medical community, every disease-causing bacterium now has various strains that are resistant to at least one of modern medicine's 100-plus pharmaceutical antibiotics. Even more unsettling is the fact that some strains resist every single antibiotic but one, and strains of three potentially life-threatening bacteria—*Enterococcus faecalis, Mycobacterium tuberculosis* and *Psuedomonas aeruginosa*—are resistant to medicine's entire pharmaceutical antibiotic arsenal. An example of the seriousness of the problem is that drug-resistant tuberculosis, caused by a bacterium, now accounts for one out of every seven new cases of TB, and 5% of these patients do not survive.[74] The World Health Organization recently announced that in future years there will be a world-wide epidemic, with tens of millions of people dying of drug-resistant tuberculosis.[75]

Another discouraging example is the bacterium *Staphylococcus aureus*, the microbe responsible for some pneumonias and for blood poisoning in surgical wounds. Approximately 40% of *Staphylococcus aureus* in the hospital setting was for some time resistant to every antibiotic but one—vancomycin. In 1994, Dr. Thomas Beam of the Veterans Administration Medical Center in Buffalo, NY stated:

> We know at some point vancomycin will succumb and the bacteria will grow and proliferate unrestrained. It will be like the 1950s and 1960s when we had nothing to treat this infection, and the mortality rates were as high as 80%.[76]

Each year during those decades, thousands of people died of staphylococcus infections. Once staph develops the gene for vancomycin resistance, warned Dr. Richard Roberts of Cornell Medical School in 1994, "we will really, really have a problem. Vancomycin is the last line [of defense]."[77] In 1997, that fearful event finally happened. In three different geographical locations, *Staphylococcus aureus* showed signs of vancomycin resistance. Dr. Stuart Levy then commented, "Emergence of forms [of *Staphylococcus aureus*] lacking sensitivity to vancomycin signifies that varieties untreatable by every known antibiotic are on their way."[78]

In 1969, U.S. Surgeon General William Stewart testified before Congress that modern medicines were in such control over the cause of disease that it was time to "close the door on infectious disease." During the 1970s-1980s, the perception was that modern medicine had conquered almost every infectious disease. Instead, "medicine's purported triumph over infectious disease has become an illusion," says Dr. Sherwin Nuland in his best-selling book *How We Die: Reflections on Life's Final Chapter.*[79] This is evidenced by the recent 58% rise in infectious diseases between 1980 and 1992[80] to become one of the top-five causes of death in the U.S.

When antibiotics are placed into animal feed and water to promote growth, subclinical amounts too small to combat infection are administered over a period of weeks or months. This creates a perfect breeding ground for antibiotic-resistant strains of microorganisms to prosper.[81] Farm animals receive an average of 30 times more antibiotics than humans[82] and antibiotic residues as well as resistant strains of microbes can remain in the animals' flesh and byproducts. Milk, for example, is allowed to contain a certain "acceptable" concentration of 80 different antibiotics,[83] most of which are used to treat bovine infection. In 1992, the General Accounting Office of the U.S. Congress found that individual states test for only four of the 80 federally-regulated antibiotics, and that unacceptable levels of 64 different drugs were found in the samples tested.[84] The unfortunate reality is that humans can acquire both antibiotic residues and resistant strains of microbes by consuming animal products such as meat, eggs, milk, cheese and a host of other byproducts.

In summary, when a person contracts an illness caused by a pathogen such as a bacterium, if the pathogen is resistant to antibiotic treatment, severe illness or death can result. Also, many people who have consumed meat or animal byproducts have antibiotic-resistant microbes present as part of the bacterial flora that populate their intestinal tracts. These potentially harmful bacteria are held in abeyance by the presence of many varieties of healthy bacteria such as *Lactobacillus acidophilus* and *Bifido bacterium*. However, if antibiotic treatment were ever required for any reason, the population of non-resistant, beneficial intestinal bacteria could be significantly reduced, allowing the resistant, harmful organisms to multiply without restraint.

It is for these reasons that as early as 1969, Great Britain and now the European Community have restricted the chronic use of antibiotics in animal feed. In 1970, an 11-man FDA committee studied the issue of microbe resistance to antibiotics and reported that no additional restrictions should be enforced in the U.S concerning the present widespread use of these drugs in animal feed.[85] In the years following, many attempts have been made, some by the FDA itself, to reduce the use of antibiotics in animal feed. Every time the issue is raised, drug and livestock lobbyists exert pressure on Congressional representatives to prevent any change. In 1977, the FDA formally proposed the banning of penicillin and tetracycline in animal feed. On many occasions since that time Congress has tacked a provision onto the FDA's appropriation, advising the FDA not to act on the issue until more conclusive evidence between resistant pathogens and human disease is found.[86]

In early 2002, talks began yet *again* about reducing the number and quantity of antibiotics used in animal farming—especially the group of quinolone antibiotics. As of this writing, no new laws have been passed.

For additional information on the subject of antibiotic-resistant super-bugs, read Jeffrey Fisher's 1994 book, *Plague Makers: How We Are Creating Catastrophic New Epidemics, and What*

We Must Do to Avert Them; or Dr. Stuart Levy's *The Antibiotic Paradox: How Miracle Drugs are Destroying the Miracle.*

Chapter Six

Food-borne Pathogens

The manner in which animals are presently raised for food production bears little resemblance to methods employed 100 years ago, even 50 years ago. Just as the sector of processed foods agglomerated into a handful of monopolies controlling production, the other sectors of the food production industry have similarly consolidated, including the animal "manufacturing" industry. Animals are raised for slaughter in facilities that are truly "animal factories," the goal of which is to produce the largest (heaviest) animal in the shortest amount of time, in the least expensive manner possible. The bottom line is the margin of profit, with issues of health and safety scoring, again, a distant second place.

The famed Indian teacher and pacifist Mahatma Ghandi remarked, "The greatness of a nation can be judged by the way its animals are treated." Intuitively, there must be some veracity to this statement. Nevertheless, people who eat meat, e.g., beef, pork, lamb, chicken, fish, etc. (yes, chicken and fish are not vegetables...), apparently believe the great variety of sentient life on Earth has been placed here to be consumed by man. Obviously, especially with today's methods of animal production, the animals suffer a great deal for most of their lives during their relatively short stays in the animal factories. In fact, many confirmed meat-eaters would be aghast at the practices of modern factory farming.

Some people don't consider these issues to be particularly germane to their everyday lives. Others are unaware of the extent of cruelty associated with harvesting animal flesh. A small clue regarding the level of cruelty involved in animal food production is that slaughterhouse workers have the highest turnover rate of any occupation in the U.S. As for the rest of us, we don't have to consider where the meat comes from. All the killing is done far away, by someone else. Some people, no doubt, think that hamburger patties are plucked from the vine, or perhaps they are netted from the sea. Although these issues could be the subject of much debate, as could the issue of vegetarianism versus meat-eating, the present focus is the investigation of the safety and health ramifications related to consuming certain foods and, in this case, consuming meat.

Foods from animal sources are subject to contamination by many types of pathogens (infective agents). The government's General Accounting Office reports that up to 81 million Americans experience some type of food-borne illness causing 9,000 deaths annually[1]—that's roughly 25 deaths per day. Contamination is largely the result of the physical conditions in which the animals are housed, their diet, and the wide range of drugs used to increase growth rate and keep them alive. Former president of the Food Animal Concerns Trust, Robert Brown, stated:

> Animal diseases on farms have consequences that come directly into our homes, bringing disease and death to people too. A rise in deadly food-borne pathogens has accompanied the introduction of factory farming. In the 1980s three new bacteria emerged as serious public health problems—Campylobacter jejuni, E. coli O157:H7, and Salmonella enteritidis...These diseases for the most part do not make the animal sick, but they cause deadly illnesses when passed on to humans.[2]

Poultry. Over nine billion fowl (including chickens, turkeys and ducks) are slaughtered in the U.S. each year. In addition, approximately 30 million male chicks each year are thrown into garbage bags to die. They simply have no economic value either as meat or to produce eggs.

In 1960, roughly 300 companies marketed chickens commercially. Currently there are less than 50 U.S. producers, of which approximately 20 companies process millions of tons annually.[3] The chickens housed in a typical egg factory number about 80,000 per warehouse. Some farms are so large that more than two million eggs are laid daily by three million hens which are housed five per each 16 x 18 inch cage.[4] The animals are fed a laboratory-produced diet laced with antibiotics, the goal of which is to increase production while reducing expense, even at the risk of producing unhealthy animals. Diets of chickens also include remains (inexpensive protein) of possibly diseased and otherwise contaminated chickens—chickens eating chickens. John Robbins writes:

> Broilers fetch a price according to their weight, not according to their health, so their diet is selected purely for its ability to maximize their weight as cheaply as possible. Similarly, the diet fed to layers is selected strictly for its ability to stimulate egg production at the lowest possible cost...As a result, these are not the healthiest animals you could find...These poor animals are riddled with disease. In fact, due to the danger of contracting disease from chickens, the Bureau of Labor has listed the poultry processing industry as one of the most hazardous of all occupations...[5] A government report found that over 90% of the chickens from most of the flocks in the country are infected with chicken cancer (leukosis).[6]

The USDA understands the level of contamination fostered by factory farming practices, and publishes a pamphlet describing the proper methods of preparing poultry for consumption. According to the USDA, raw poultry even in its packaging, should not be handled without wearing either plastic or latex gloves. After preparing the meat, the kitchen counter, sink and cutting utensils should be washed with a solution of chlorine bleach.

The *Atlanta Journal-Constitution* recently interviewed 84 federal poultry inspectors employed at 37 processing plants throughout the states of Alabama, Arkansas, Georgia, Mississippi and North Carolina. Included were inspectors at plants operated by the eight largest poultry producers in the U.S.

> Every week...millions of chickens leaking yellow pus, stained by green feces, contaminated by harmful bacteria, or marred by lung and heart infection, cancerous tumors or skin conditions are shipped for sale to consumers, instead of being condemned and destroyed, the USDA inspectors said.[7]

Comfortingly, the USDA and industry executives told *The Journal-Constitution* that the poultry is safe to eat as long as it is cooked thoroughly. Whew! Another sigh of relief. Unfortunately, that didn't convince everyone. At least 70% of the USDA inspectors interviewed stated they were so concerned about the present state of the industry they no longer eat poultry.[8]

According to the USDA, up to 80% of U.S. poultry is contaminated with salmonella bacteria and up to 98% is contaminated with *Campylobacter jejuni*. "The average chicken you buy today in any store has enough Campylobactor on it to make 1,000 people very sick," USDA microbiologist Dr. Norman Stern told *The Journal-Constitution*.[9] The only step that stands between you and illness or worse is the proper preparation of the poultry.

The National Institutes of Health reported in 1994 that a variety of retroviruses are prevalent in U.S. chickens and turkeys raised on factory farms. (HIV, the virus thought to cause AIDS, is another type of retrovirus.) The NIH stated that some commercial chickens test positive for retrovirus antibodies, and some animals actually carry infectious viruses. These retroviruses may be present in poultry products and also in eggs.[10] (One hundred million such viral particles can fit in the space of the period that follows this sentence. A single viral particle is capable of changing a healthy cell into a cancerous cell.) To date, the link between poultry retroviruses and human cancer is incomplete, but further study of the issue is imperative. Further reading can be done at www.upc-online.org, the Web site of United Poultry Concerns, Inc. Also informative are the following books, both available from United Poultry Concerns (757)678-7875: Karen Davis, Ph. D's 1997 *Prisoned Chickens, Poisoned Eggs: An Inside Look at the Modern Poultry Industry*; and attorney David Wolfson's 1999 *Beyond the Law: Agribusiness and the Systematic Abuse of Animals Raised for Food and Food Production.*

Swine. In terms of a healthful product, pigs fare little better than poultry, although the number of slaughtered animals is far lower due to their larger size. (Too bad chickens don't weigh 200 pounds—but don't hold your breath. That more corpulent version is probably on someone's drawing board.) In the U.S., some 100 million pigs surrender their lives each year for the pleasure of our appetites.

Some of the largest swine factories are huge complexes housing more than 100,000 animals. As is the case with other factory-produced animals, pigs are confined to such a small space they are barely able to move. On most farms, pigs are housed separately in narrow steel stalls measuring about seven square feet (approximately 3.5 x 2 feet).

The September, 1976 issue of *Hog Farm Management* advised modern pig farmers (who prefer to be called "pork production engineers"—a job description that rivals the classification of truck drivers as "commodity relocation engineers"...) to focus on the task at hand:

> Forget the pig as an animal. Treat him just like a machine in a factory. Schedule treatments like you would lubrication. Breeding season like the first step in an assembly line. And marketing like the delivery of finished goods.[11]

The March, 1978 issue of *National Hog Farmer* informed its readership that, "The breeding sow should be thought of, treated as, a valuable piece of machinery, whose function is to pump out baby pigs like a sausage machine."[12]

The latest, greatest innovation in corporate pig farming should earn its originators an A grade for their ingenuity, if not a Grade A for their product. Some of the largest swine factories in the U.S. have implemented a system of stacking tiers of caged animals on top of one another, thus conserving space and spreading the cost of the facility over a larger number of animals. Unfortunately, this is not the only item being spread using this configuration. Pigs in the upper tiers of cages contribute a continuous shower of excrement on the animals below. This fecal material can be a significant contributing factor to the spread of pathogenic bacteria and contamination of the marketed product. Cross-contamination between animals often occurs during the processing procedures as well.

Cattle. Cattle farming in the U.S. produces an even less wholesome product, if such can be the case. Some cattle farms house as many as 100,000 "units," as they are called. Although differences do exist between facilities, studies from the University of Minnesota suggest that maximum profit is obtained when each cow is housed in a space equivalent to fourteen square feet of "living" space (approximately 5 x 2.75 feet).[13] During their short lives the animals are administered an array of weight-producing hormones and antibiotics—artificially-induced obesity. (Concerned about protecting their citizens from hormone-contaminated meat, in 1989 the European Economic Community banned the importation of hormone-implanted U.S. beef.)

Awaiting their ultimate fate, cattle are fed a diet that does little to produce a healthy animal. One of the food ingredients includes possibly-contaminated and diseased cattle that did not survive long enough to be slaughtered for human consumption. Other ingredients are equally unappetizing:

> [The diet]...may include such delicacies as sawdust laced with ammonia and feathers, shredded newspapers (complete with all the colors of toxic ink from the Sunday comics and advertising circulars), "plastic hay," processed sewage, inedible tallow and grease, poultry litter [feces, by any other name, taste just as sweet], cement dust (to make the animals thirsty), and cardboard scraps, not to mention the insecticides, antibiotics and hormones... The industry recognizes

that major health problems ensue from the way today's cattle are fed. But it doesn't matter to them if the animal is ill, even if the illness is so severe it is dying, so long as it can be kept alive with drugs long enough to be slaughtered and sold to the consumer.[14]

Escherichia coli O157:H7. According to the Centers for Disease Control, 250-500 deaths a year occur from the pathogen *Escherichia coli*: O157:H7, a bacterium that has attracted considerable public attention in recent years as the result of several fast-food restaurant outbreaks. Although the bacterium is present in the feces of only a small number of cattle, cross-contamination readily occurs. Nicols Fox, author of *Spoiled: The Dangerous Truth About a Food Chain Gone Haywire*, describes the problem:

> An infected cow might shed the pathogen in the field and the next grazing cow picks it up. Even if only one or two cows in a herd were shedding the pathogen at the time of shipping, tired, frightened, and hungry cattle...attempting to keep their balance in a moving vehicle lose control of their bowels. In these tight quarters the fecal material gets on the hides of other animals. When they arrive, all the cows are filthy and distressed...Routinely cattle, massed together in tight quarters, [are] standing in the excrement of many animals...it's not surprising that O157 and other pathogens get onto meat during the slaughtering process through contamination with fecal material.[15]

Another type of cross-contamination also can occur. It is estimated that ground beef (hamburger) can be a mixture of 100 different cattle from several different countries,[16] with any infective pathogen capable of being spread throughout the product. USDA researchers estimate that one infected animal could contaminate as much as 16 tons (32,000 pounds) of hamburger meat.[17] A 1997 U.S. study indicated that over 25 million pounds of hamburger meat were contaminated by O157. Supermarket surveys of fresh meats have shown that *E. coli* O157:H7 is present in about 3.5% of ground beef, 1.5% of pork, 1.5% of poultry and 2.0% of lamb.[18] In some instances it is likely that levels of contamination are considerably higher.

In September of 1993, the USDA officially declared *E. coli* O157:H7 a meat contaminant, and further declared that a policy of testing for the bacterium would be instituted.[19] One month later, the American Meat Institute, the Food Marketing Institute, the Associated Grocers of America and four other groups filed a lawsuit against the USDA to halt its testing for the *E. coli* bacterium. The rational of these powerful trade organizations not to test their beef for the bacterium demonstrated their true concern for the consumer. If testing were required, they reasoned, customers might grow to ignore the cooking and handling warnings on the packaging (the implementation of which they fought tooth and nail), believing the meat was safe.[20] (In 1996, the USDA began testing for salmonella contamination. However, in 2001 the Fifth U.S. Circuit Court of Appeals sided with a Dallas, Texas ground beef producer whose meat was contaminated with salmonella. According to the court decision, the USDA is authorized only to prevent processors from adding contaminants to the meat. Because the meat was already contaminated with salmonella prior to its arrival at the meat processing plant, the company could not be held responsible for the contaminated meat).

Meat inspection laws in this country were enacted in 1906, and are a throwback to the 19th century. From the above two examples, it appears that government meat inspectors, as has been the case for decades, are allowed only to look, touch and smell the meat—microscopic testing *ist verboten!*

Bovine Leukemia Virus (BLV). One of the prevalent diseases of cattle is Bovine Leukemia Virus. It is believed that as many as 60% of all U.S. cattle, and in some herds up to 80%, are infected with BLV, as evidenced by the high incidence of bovine lymphosarcoma (malignant, cancerous growths affecting every organ of the body) detected at slaughter.[21] In Japan, where there is widespread infection of the human population with Human Lymphotropic Virus I (HTLV-I, the virus that causes Human T-cell Leukemia), the complete genetic sequence of BLV has been decoded and indicates an intimate relationship with HTLV-I and HTLV-II.[22] It has also been learned that mammary gland cells of cattle can have cancerous infections, in which case there can be shedding of live virus in the milk.[23]

Is BLV able to cross the species barrier and infect humans? It has been shown that BLV-infected cow's milk given to newborn chimpanzees is capable of infecting the young chimps in a very short time.[24] Does pasteurization inactivate the virus? Pasteurization does seem to destroy the infectivity of BLV in milk, but it is not known whether pasteurization destroys the activity of the proviral DNA in the infected cells.[25]

Virgil Hulse, M.D., author of the ground-breaking book *Mad Cows and Milk Gate*, has been a practicing family physician for 30 years, and has a long list of impressive credentials. He holds a Bachelor's Degree in Agriculture; a Master's Degree in Public Health (Milk and Food Technology); and a second Master's in Public Health (Cancer Epidemiology). Dr. Hulse is a former Associate Professor of Family Practice in the Medical School at Loma Linda University, and has many other accomplishments to his credit. Concerning the issue of BLV-infected milk, Dr. Hulse comments:

> It is my opinion that when you drink milk that contains these [infective] lymphocytes you are setting yourself at risk for leukemia, lymphoma, Hodgkin's disease, multiple myeloma and multiple sclerosis or other cancers related to fat such as prostate, breast, and colon cancer, even if the milk is pasteurized.[26]

Predictably, the U.S. dairy and meat industries maintain that drinking milk and eating meat infected with Bovine Leukemia Virus pose no threat to human health. Got milk? Got medical insurance? For more information on the potential dangers of consuming milk and other dairy products, call (888) NOT MILK; access www.notmilk.com; or read Robert Cohen's books *Milk: A-Z* (©2000), and *Milk: The Deadly Poison* (©1997).

How worrisome is BLV, and is there a real possibility humans could become infected by this animal disease? In 1976, the prestigious medical journal the *Lancet* reported that the higher the meat consumption in a given country, the higher the incidence of leukemia in the residents of that country.[27] This does not mean, *per se*, that meat consumption causes leukemia, but the relationship (correlation) raises a red flag. Given the fact that cancer is the leading cause of death in children ages 1-14 and that leukemia accounts for about 50% of all childhood cancer deaths, the relationship of BLV to leukemia and the consequences of this disease should not be taken lightly.

North America has the highest incidence of adult cancers, followed closely by Western Europe, Australia and New Zealand. According to the National Cancer Institute, people who consume a meat-laden diet have a 300% increased risk of esophageal cancer and a 200% increased risk of stomach cancer. Concerning meat consumption in general, some researchers believe it is the excess of protein and fat accompanying the regular consumption of meat that causes the illness and disease so characteristic of the U.S. population.

In countries whose populations consume much less meat, there is a lower incidence of most of the debilitating diseases found in this country.[28] Dr. T. Colin Campbell, a health researcher who has studied the health patterns of the Chinese, comments about meat consumption:

> ...people who eat more meat have higher blood cholesterol levels and higher blood albumin levels, which is a function of protein intake. As blood levels of albumin and cholesterol go up, the diseases we get in the West—cancer, heart disease and diabetes—also start going up. It's quite remarkable.[29]

Bovine Immunodeficiency Virus (BIV). Another disease related to the cattle industry is the retrovirus Bovine Immunodeficiency Virus, a relatively recently-discovered and widespread disease similar to Human Immunodeficiency Virus (HIV), the virus thought to cause AIDS in humans. BIV has genes, antibodies and a physical structure similar to HIV, and can cause impairment of the immune system and chronic or lethal diseases in cattle as HIV does in humans. Observed symptoms include enlarged lymph nodes; brain and spinal cord lesions; progressive weakness; weight loss; respiratory infections; and a general wasting away frequently followed by death.

The incidence of BIV infection is high, with average frequencies of 40% in beef and 64% in dairy herds found in Louisiana and 50% of all herds examined in Mississippi.[30] A high percentage of BIV-infected animals also test seropositive for BLV.[31] First isolated in cattle in 1970, BIV has been shown to transfer infection among goats, sheep and rabbits via a blood-borne route.[32] Furthermore, scientists have demonstrated that human cells can be infected with BIV.[33] The USDA reports it is not certain "whether exposure to BIV proteins causes human sera to...become HIV positive."[34]

Bovine Spongiform Encephalopathy (BSE). Popularly known as Mad Cow Disease, some researchers believe BSE is so threatening it may one day eclipse AIDS as a killer of humans. For this reason, the present section on BSE is considerably more lengthy in comparison to other topics we discuss. BSE was first observed in British cattle as early as 1985. The symptoms of the disease mimic those of the disease *scrapie* which is found in sheep, so named because infected animals tend to scrape themselves against fences, walls and other objects. Scrapie in sheep is a neurological disorder characterized by the "staggers" (lack of coordination), behavioral changes and, as the disease progresses, microscopic holes form in the brain giving it a sponge-like consistency, hence the term "spongiform."

Scrapie has been known for some 200 years, and has been present in the U.S. since 1947. The USDA reports that 7,500 sheep in 39 states in the U.S. are infected with scrapie.[35] In 1952 a voluntary eradication program was launched, but this was found to be ineffective. A compulsory eradication program was then enacted which some years later was discontinued by the USDA "because it would be perceived by the public that it [scrapie] was a threat to health."[36] Although there is no conclusive evidence that scrapie is a public health threat, at the least it could be upsetting to a consumer to realize that the animal upon which he is supping may have died from a disease that rotted the animal's brain and spinal cord.

The cause of both Mad Cow Disease and scrapie is believed by many/most BSE researchers to be an infective agent called a *prion*—rhymes with neon. The prion theory was originally proposed in 1982 by University of California-San Francisco biochemist Dr. Stanley Prusiner, for which he was awarded a Nobel Prize. The prion is thought to be not a virus or bacteria, but a protein particle gone awry. It is assumed to be many times smaller than a viral particle[37] since it passes through filtering techniques which are able to detect most viruses.

There are, however, other interesting theories put forth by scientists of considerable repute. One such theory is the brainchild of Anthony R. Parish, Ph. D., a Fellow of the New York Academy of Sciences and recently selected to be included in *Who's Who in the World* (2001) in recognition for his many years as a leading medical researcher. Dr. Parish believes animals are being poisoned by industrial chemicals, and the poisons are further transmitted to the offspring. Prions, he believes, are merely symptoms of the underlying cause. You can read more about Dr. Parish's theory at www.onshop.co.uk/bse/us_bse.htm.

Also on the chemical bandwagon is British organic farmer Mark Purdy. Purdy believes BSE was caused by the compulsory spraying of organophosphate pesticides such as phosmet to combat a British plague of Warble fly. These chemicals, in turn, activated a prion mutation in cattle. Purdy also believes the mineral manganese is a co-factor. He found that high levels of manganese were sprayed on the British cattle along with the pesticides. He further discovered that infected clusters of U.S. deer and elk have an association with high levels of manganese. Purdy's view is that because of the huge potential liability of the chemical companies involved, the true causal agent will never see the light of day.

The particle, call it a prion or by any other name, is thought to be a totally new infective agent having no DNA or RNA. Deadly nevertheless, the spongiform diseases caused by these agents can be transferred to other species both by injection and orally.[38] Their infectivity cannot be destroyed even at temperatures of 360 degrees Celsius, and they also appear to be resistant to radiation and most disinfectants (including bleach).[39] Infected animals have been buried for up to three years and upon exhumation, their remains are still infectious.[40]

The most infective parts of affected animals are referred to as the offal (appropriately pronounced "awful"), which consists of any tissues of the brain, spinal cord, spleen, thymus, tonsil, lymph nodes and intestines. Blood also has been shown to be infective. Other tissues also could transmit infection.

For decades, producers of food animals have incorporated the remains of sheep, chickens and cows into the animal feed of cattle as well as other animals. Many of the animals rendered into animal feed are diseased with infectious agents such as scrapie. It is now generally accepted (with certain notable exceptions, as mentioned) that Bovine Spongiform Encephalopathy, or Mad Cow Disease, originated as the result of cattle being fed scrapie-infected sheep, including the byproducts of infected sheep such as bone meal (which is often an ingredient of pet food). In an effort to avoid waste and inexpensively produce animals for human consumption, every bit of an animal is recycled for use. Dr. Raymond Burns, head of the alternative uses program of the Kansas Department of Agriculture told *The New York Times* in a 1996 interview, "We use everything but the squeal, the cluck, and the moo."[41] And in some cases, diseases are thrown in at no extra charge.

About four billion pounds per year of "inedible" parts from cows, chickens, pigs, road kill and other animals are ground down and recycled back into animal feed in the form of meat, bone meal and blood meal.[42] Tallow and gelatin are also produced in this process. About 30% of the recycled product is used in pet food, 30% in chicken feed, 20% in pig feed and the remainder in feed for beef and dairy cattle.[43] It is simply a matter of economics. Also—and don't let Bowser or Buttercup read this—it's standard practice for some rendering plants to recycle house pets back into animal food. According to a 1997 *New York Times* article, each month the city of Los Angeles alone ships 200 tons of euthanized dogs and cats to rendering plants to be recycled back into animal food.[44] [For more fun reading on the subject of recycled house pets, Ann Martin's books *Food Pets Die For: Shocking Facts About Pet Food* (©2000), and *Protect Your Pet: More Shocking Facts* (©2001) are excellent resources; contact New Sage Press, (877)695-2211; www.newsagepress.com]

Cattle that die from either known or unknown causes are called "downer" cows, and constitute a group known as 4-D animals: dead, dying, diseased and disabled, the majority of which are recycled into animal feed. Before the outbreak of Mad Cow Disease in Britain in the mid 1980s, the recycling of animals into animal feed was considered a trade secret of the feed companies.[45] Now, world-wide attention has been focused on the practice—because it's clear the human food chain is being affected.

The lack of American media exposure to these important albeit controversial subjects should signal some cause for concern, particularly when issues involving public health go unreported or under reported. For over a decade, Britain and the European Community have been afire with the Mad Cow controversy and the human deaths that are believed to be the result of eating contaminated beef. Although to date the human death toll has reached about 100 (most being permanent or temporary residents of Britain), Britain has slaughtered upward of five million cows infected or believed to be infected with BSE, at an expense of billions of dollars. (In a gesture of helpfulness the Cambodian government has suggested that, as an alternative to incinerating these millions of infected animals, they be used to detonate some of the 10 million land mines, about 140 mines per square mile, that remain undetonated following the Cambodian civil war.)

Over 180,000 BSE cases have been documented in Britain to date, and more than 70 cases per week were being reported as of 1996.[46] After that time the incidence has declined dramatically, with only 30 cases being reported throughout Europe in 1999. In the year 2000, however, the incidence surged slightly to more than 100 cases,[47] which has once again run the red flag up the pole. To date, BSE has spread to cattle in Austria, Belgium, Denmark, France, Germany, Holland, Italy, Ireland, Liechtenstein, Luxembourg, Poland, Portugal, Spain, Switzerland, Sweden, Japan and Britain. Britain, however, remains the focal point of the outbreak.

When the disease first struck, England's top scientists were fearful of what the future could bring. Thames Valley University Professor of Food Policy Tim Lang stated:

> We are in a mass experiment which is killing us. Never before have diseased ruminants (sheep) been fed to other ruminants (cows) and then fed to humans. We have interfered with the whole process of nature and what is now happening is one of our worst nightmares. This is a tragedy on a massive scale. The Government has been so totally stupid. Even now they are still employing crisis management techniques and damage limitation exercises.[48]

Microbiologist Richard Lacey of Leeds University stated:

> ...we are now estimating that next [21st] century the typical number of...human cases will run at between 5,000 and 500,000 a year..The only logical approach for the human population in the United Kingdom is to avoid all beef products.[49]

Dr. Lacy's colleague, Dr. Stephan Dealler of Leads University Medical School, believes that "no one who knows enough about this subject would feed their daughter a beef burger."[50] It is Dr. Dealler's opinion that those eating infected meat have a 50/50 chance of acquiring spongiform encephelopathy. In an article published in the *British Food Journal*, Dr. Dealler stated that by the year 2001, most adult British meat-eaters will have ingested a potentially fatal dose of BSE-infected beef,[51] which could be as small as one gram of infected meat.[52] (One gram is the approximate weight of half of one U.S. dime.) Other researchers believe that infection may be transmitted by as little as one or two infective molecules, depending on the state of a person's immune system.

It is unfortunate to note that during the years 1982 to 1992, roughly 13 tons of meat, bone meal and other meat-related by-products implicated in the British epidemic were imported by the U.S. from Britian.[53] It is humorous to note that after the news of the initial human spongiform cases in Britain, the burger giant McDonald's posted window signs advertising "veggie" burgers instead of beef[54]—such was the uproar about Mad Cow Disease and its potential to infect the human population. Did somebody say McVeggie?

Contributing further to the uneasiness is the fact that about 100 cats in Britain have died from feline spongiform encephelopathy, presumably the result of eating contaminated pet food.[55] The spongiform disease also has infected mice and pigs, as well as zoo animals such as antelope, cheetah, eland, elk, kudu, marmoset, ocelot, ostrich and puma,[56] all presumably infected from feed contaminated with BSE.

In the U.S., a form of transmissible spongiform encephalopathy (TSE) is being found in other animal populations as well. Referred to as chronic wasting disease (CWD), it has been found in white-tailed deer, mule deer and elk in Colorado and Wyoming, and mule deer in Nebraska and Saskatchewan, Canada. CWD also has been found in captive elk herds in Colorado, Montana, Oklahoma, South Dakota, Nebraska, and Saskatchewan as well as in captive white-tailed deer in South Dakota.

The human counterpart of BSE is called Creutzfeldt-Jacob (Croits-felt Yaw-cob) Disease (CJD), and the symptoms are similar to those observed in cattle. Apparently there is at least one new strain or variation of CJD, manifesting with slightly different symptoms. This new variation is labeled nvCJD, or new variant CJD (also called vCJD). There can be a long incubation period for CJD, producing a latency period of as long as 20-40 years before symptoms manifest,[57] although symptoms typically manifest much sooner.

No doubt many Americans are aware of Mad Cow Disease, although it has received surprisingly little press coverage in the

U.S. in comparison to the magnitude of the story. The exception to this, as mentioned, was coverage of the Oprah Winfrey trial, the culmination of a lawsuit brought by Texas cattlemen against Ms. Winfrey. During her television program which aired April 16, 1996, after learning some of the facts surrounding Mad Cow Disease Oprah exclaimed, "It just stopped me cold from eating another burger."[58] The trial did not provoke the U.S. press to engage in dialogue concerning the difficult questions surrounding BSE including its possible transmission to humans. Rather, the media side-stepped the issue in favor of vacuous nightly discussions of the trial in a manner characteristic of American journalism of the late 20th century.

Do Mad Cow Disease and CJD pose a threat to the health of Americans? Many related to the U.S. beef industry say, "No way!" However, it may be wise to take a lesson from the Brits. In 1988, the British established a prestigious committee of scientists to evaluate the potential health threat in England. The Southwood Committee reported that it is "most unlikely that BSE will have any implications for human health."[59] The British are now whistling a different tune. In March of 1996, the government-convened Lord Phillips Inquiry stated as many as 136,000 people could lose their lives to vCJD. Since the time of that Inquiry, the Blair administration has upped the estimate to as many as 250,000, and believes the worst case scenario is one out of every 250 British citizens dying from CJD.

Noted scrapie specialist Dr. R.F. Marsh of the School of Veterinary Medicine at the University of Wisconsin stated that the U.S. already has its own form of Mad Cow Disease. Dr. Prusiner, the premier proponent of prions, agrees with Dr. Marsh.[60] Adding to this view Dr. Joseph Gibbs, a researcher at the U.S. National Institutes of Health, has stated, "I'm convinced that BSE has occurred here."[61] Most serious BSE researchers agree with Marsh, Prusiner, and Gibbs. In vehement disagreement with these views—insisting that BSE is not a problem in the U.S.—is the

$150 billion per year U.S. cattle industry which slaughters over 40 million cows annually.

The infection of U.S. cattle could be the result of recycling 4-D cows back into the food of living cows.[62] Dr. Marsh estimated that in Wisconsin alone, 35,000 downers per year have been shipped to renderers who supply the recycled protein product for use in animal feed.[63] It is a fact that in this country there is an incidence of hundreds of thousands of downer cows in a given year.[64] Some have estimated the incidence to be as high as 15,000 per day. Not all downer cows are recycled into animal food. Some are sold as human food—principally, ground beef. It is estimated that up to 400,000 people could be infected by a single infected animal entering the food chain.[65]

An incident that occurred in 1985 at a Stentsonville, Wisconsin mink ranch gives support to Dr. Marsh's beliefs concerning transmission of BSE via downer cows. All the minks at this ranch were destroyed as the result of Transmissible Mink Encephelopathy (TME) after consuming a diet consisting of more than 95% downer cows.[66] It is also known that spongiform encephelopathy has been transmitted to laboratory chimpanzees and pigs, and researchers believe there is the potential of crossing other species barriers.[67]

Dr. Paul Brown, a leading CJD researcher at the U.S. National Institutes of Health, believes that humans may be able to contract BSE by eating either infected meat, meat byproducts or by contact with products containing infected animal ingredients.[68] Products such as facial creams, moisturizers, shampoos, gelatin (including the gelatin used to encapsulate many nutritional supplements and pharmaceuticals) and even floor wax contain animal ingredients that are potentially infective, although there is no hard evidence that CJD can be acquired in this manner.[69]

On October 20, 2000, the United Kingdom Department of Health issued a recall notice for oral polio vaccines produced by the British manufacturer Medeva, near Liverpool. The Department of Health was concerned that Medeva used potentially-BSE-infected material from British cattle in 11 million doses of polio vaccine that have been administered to children and adults over the last decade. The problems surrounding the polio vaccine could be merely the tip of the iceberg. Medeva also manufactures vaccines for flu, tuberculosis, tetanus and hepatitis B. Medeva's Fluvirin® has been used by some 20 million unsuspecting Americans. U.K. Liberal Democrat Norman Baker stated:

> The Department of Health and the MCA [U.K. Medicines Control Agency] have completely failed to act in the interest of public health. In their desperate attempts not to undermine the vaccination program, they have tried to sweep all problems under the carpet. As a result, public confidence has been shattered. When will they learn that the answer is not to cover up, but to identify problems and deal with them immediately?[70]

Shortly thereafter, the Canadian Broadcasting Corporation announced the Canadian government is studying whether or not BSE could exist in products that contain beef byproducts such as vaccines and cosmetics. Several childhood vaccines, including diphtheria, tetanus and polio, contain bovine byproducts.[71] Virtually *all* vaccines (whether or not they are grown in tissue cultures that include tissue from bovine sources, which some are) are nourished (fed) with bovine fetal cells.

[A short digression into the nature of vaccinations. Although vaccines are not usually thought of as food, they do represent a modern advent which is placed directly into the body. In addition to the above-mentioned problem of BSE contamination, it is now widely recognized by many researchers that vaccines are plagued by contamination from other sources as well, including preservatives such as formaldehyde, mercury and polysorbate. Also, because of their intimate contact with animal material, vaccines often are contaminated with harmful microbes such as viruses. In addition, miscellaneous animal-sourced fragments of RNA and DNA can be contained within the finished vaccine, forming latent proviruses that can later become activated as diseases such as cancer, lupus and arthritis.[72]

There is a further fact relating to vaccinations that is often overlooked—especially by the allopathic medical community, not to mention a large percentage of the unknowing public. Namely, the efficacy of vaccinations is seriously in question, despite all of the (largely-government-sponsored) advertising to the contrary. In other words, do vaccines really work? Are they able to confer immunity to humans against the diseases they are designed to combat? The answer to this question is controversial, but many within the medical research community believe that vaccines are ineffective—in fact, they do not work as proposed (and advertised). In spite of the fact that vaccines are heavily promoted by trade organizations such as the American Medical Association, and government agencies such as the National Institutes of Health (NIH), CDC, FDA, and the World Health Organization (WHO), there are many reasons to believe they are ineffective, if not harmful.

Most people view vaccines as a modern wonder medicine that has rescued humanity from the ravages of many once-highly-feared diseases—including smallpox, diphtheria, pertussis (whooping cough), tetanus, measles, and influenza. A more thorough investigation paints a different picture altogether. If one examines the annual incidence from 1900 to present of the many diseases for which vaccines are available, a most revealing pattern jumps straight off the paper. All of the diseases, without exception, show a steady decline from 1900, continuing to decline directly through the points at which these vaccines were introduced, up to the present. In fact, by the time these vaccines were introduced (mostly from the mid-1940s to the mid-1960s), *the diseases they were designed to fight were almost nonexistent.*

Improved nutrition and sanitary conditions are generally believed to be the reasons for this gradual but steady decline in the incidence of most diseases against which we continue to vaccinate. "Twenty vaccines by the age of two!" says Uncle Sam, whose activities help support a multi-billion dollar per year industry. For more information on what some have called murder by injection, contact the National Vaccine Information Center at (800)909-shot, or www.909shot.com; also, the Alternative Medicine site is an excellent resource on a multiplicity of topics, www.alternativemedicine.com; Dr. Len Horowitz' audio cassette *Horowitz 'On Vaccines'* (800)508-4787; good books include Alan Phillips' *Dispelling Vaccination Myths*; Neil Miller's *Immunization: Theory vs. Reality*; and Viera Schreibner's *Vaccinations: 100 Years of Orthodox Research Shows that Vaccines Represent a Medical Assault on the Immune System*; also see www.nccn.net/~wwithin/vaccine.htm]

Now, back to the beef. Although there have been only several reported cases (by the establishment media) of CJD in the U.S. that appear to be caused by consuming infected beef, the typical 10-40 year incubation period before symptoms manifest probably masks the true incidence of the disease. Also, many researchers believe that CJD is being mistaken and mis-diagnosed for other diseases such as multiple sclerosis, dementia, viral infections and Alzheimer's disease. Today, about 25% of Americans over the age of 65 have Alzheimer's, and nearly 50% who live beyond 70 years will develop some form of dementia during their lifetimes.

In July of 1990, an editorial in the *Lancet* suggested that CJD is often mis-diagnosed for Alzheimer's. The authors of this editorial suggest that whereas 30-40 cases per year of CJD in Britain are documented, a more accurate figure would be 4,500.[73] The symptoms of CJD and Alzheimer's are similar: demented behavior and steadily increasing lack of coordination followed by death. Autopsied victims' brains are found to be shrunken and riddled with microscopic holes.

In 1989, doctors at the Veterans Administration Hospital in Pittsburgh, Pennsylvania consecutively autopsied 54 patients who had been demented. They discovered three of these patients had been victims of CJD—a rate of about 1,000 times higher than expected.[74] Additionally, Gareth Roberts, an Alzheimer's and dementia expert for SmithKline Beecham Pharmaceuticals, reviewed brain samples of 1000 patients collected from 1964 to 1990. Roberts found 19 CJD cases upon reexamination, whereas only 11 had been detected initially. This represents a 40% error in misdiagnosing CJD patients.[75]

Until recently, an autopsy was the only means of confirming the presence of BSE. In early 2002, a patent was issued to the British biotech firm Proteome Sciences, Plc, for the detection of BSE in the blood of humans or animals. The test works by detecting changes in the prion proteins that accompany BSE infection. Several other biotech companies are also pursuing a BSE blood test.

For over a decade scientists, physicians, citizen's groups and even some government agencies have recommended to the FDA and USDA that a ban be instituted on feeding ruminants to ruminants. In 1993, the Foundation for Economic Trends petitioned the FDA to stop the practice of feeding ruminant animal protein to animals. In 1994 the FDA seemed to agree that such a ban was necessary, and published a proposed ban in the Federal Register. The ban was shouted down by the rendering and livestock industries. The USDA's Animal and Plant Inspection Service (APHIS) explained that "the cost to the livestock and rendering industries would be substantial" and that a change in the present policy "could pose major problems for the U.S. livestock and rendering industries."[76]

In October of 1997, the U.S. FDA finally enacted a ban on ruminant-to-ruminant feeding, although many BSE experts believe the regulation as it is presently set forth is a case of too little, too late. Critics of the ban suggest the ruling has serious shortcomings: [77]

♦ Cow tallow (solid fat) and cow blood are allowed to be fed to cattle.

♦ Pigs, chickens and horses are allowed to be fed to their own species.

♦ Pigs, chickens and horses are allowed to be fed to cattle.

♦ Known spongiform-infected animals are allowed to be used in feeds for chickens, pigs, farmed fish as well as—look out Fido and Fluffy—pet food.

♦ It will probably be several years before all the beef available in the U.S. market is free from exposure to ruminant protein.

Before the U.S. ban was enacted, a National Institutes of Health Advisory Panel recommended to the FDA that a total ban on all mammalian protein in animal feed be instituted, as the European Union has recently put into place. Given the magnitude of the potential threat to large segments of the meat-eating population in the U.S., the enactment of more stringent regulations for recycled meats would seem to be a no-brainer—which makes one wonder what kinds of foods our lawmakers have been eating.

An article in the March, 1998 *Seattle Weekly* newspaper concluded their treatise on Mad Cow Disease with the following words:

> For the time being, we'll dally with partial bans and uncertain risk reduction while the price of not being careful enough is slowly tallied in England. There, the unleashed prions are silently burrowing their way through the brains of an unknown number of future victims.[78]

To learn more about Mad Cow Disease, access www.madcow.org; www.purefood.org/madcow.htm; or read Sheldon Rampton and John Stauber's 1997 book, *Mad Cow U.S.A.: Could the Nightmare Happen Here?*

Seafood. It is difficult to locate a sizable body of water anywhere on Earth that is not polluted. In many cases fishing in coastal waters, inland lakes, and rivers is no longer permitted. When it is, consumers are taking a serious risk. The sources of pollution include heavy industry, government facilities, and municipalities. A recent EPA study found over 600 industrial polluters, including metal manufacturers; pulp and paper mills; petroleum refineries; and organic chemicals, plastics and synthetics manufacturing.

Twelve federal installations were named including military bases and the Department of Energy nuclear plants. Over 240 municipalities were also named.[79]

Because of the intimacy of contact with its polluted environment, seafood has the broadest range of contamination of any food. Not only is it subject to contamination by viruses and bacteria contained in the water, seafood is also susceptible to contamination from cadmium, dioxins, mercury, pesticides, polychlorinated byphenols (PCBs), polyether compounds, and poison-producing organisms called dinoflagellates.

Seafood concentrates pollutants to much higher levels than the concentrations found in the surrounding water. Oysters and clams, for example, have been shown to concentrate viruses and bacteria up to 60 times the levels found in their environments.[80] The EPA estimates that fish can concentrate PCBs up to nine million times the amount found in their environment.[81] Because of the extent of contamination of the seafood supply, it would be prudent to avoid consuming the following:[82]

♦ Seafood harvested from coastal waters, inland lakes, and inland rivers

♦ Predatory fish high on the food chain: bass, marlin, pike, shark, swordfish and tuna

♦ Bottom feeders that are susceptible to toxic sediment: catfish, carp and flounder

♦ Migratory fish that are vulnerable to costal pollution: Atlantic sturgeon, bluefish, mackerel, salmon and striped bass

♦ Products of aquaculture (fish farms) such as carp, catfish, salmon and trout. About 40% of the oysters, almost all rainbow trout, and over 10% of all the seafood eaten in the U.S. are produced by aquatic farms that may use antibiotics, hormones, pesticides and vaccines without disclosing these practices.[83]

♦ Shellfish such as clams, crab, lobster, mussels, oysters and scallops which are particularly susceptible to coastal pollution

♦ Seafood harvested from freshwater lakes such as the Great Lakes. The Genesse County Medical Society of Michigan stated that Great Lakes' fish should not be eaten by "children or by men and women who ever plan to have children."

Factory-farmed animals, including cattle and poultry, consume about 50% of the world's fish catch.[84] These animals and their byproducts such as dairy products and eggs, are therefore subject to contamination from the contaminated fish meal they consume.

Several years ago a new infective microorganism emerged off the shores of North Carolina, and is now present as far north as Chesapeake Bay and beyond.[85] Sharing some characteristic of both plants and animals, *Pfiesteria piscicida* is contaminating local seafood as well as directly infecting humans with seriously debilitating symptoms such as immune disorders, as well as bleeding sores, stomach cramps, respiratory constriction, disorientation and memory loss. Researchers believe this organism has likely always been present in the ocean, but only recently has become activated by the high levels of chemical contamination. The organism produces lesions on fish, disfigurement, and often causes fish kills of large proportions. Some scientists believe that *Pfiesteria* has the potential to unleash an environmental incident of catastrophic proportions. People who have witnessed the damaging effects of *Pfiesteria* have nicknamed the organism "the cell from hell."

In 1992, Drs. Joshua Lederberg and Robert Shope of the National Academy of Sciences published *Emerging Infections: Microbial Threats to Health in the United States.* They believe that in the near future modern civilization is likely to encounter epidemics of diseases caused by microbial pathogens—epidemics which could rival the 1918 pandemic of influenza in which millions people died within a one year period.[86] Support is given to their belief by the emergence of a variety of new, infective, food-borne microorganisms that were totally nonthreatening just 20 years ago. Included among these are *Yersinia enterococlitica, Campylobactor jejuni, Listeria monocytogenes, Escherichia coli* O157:H7 (hemorrhagic *E. coli*), *Pfiesteria, Cryptosporidium,* and more.

Symptoms of these pathogenic infections range from nausea, diarrhea, vomiting, cramps, and fever on the one hand, to more serious maladies including ulcers, arthritis, urinary tract infections, meningitis, stillbirths, severe chronic physical impairment and even death. As mentioned previously, up to 81 million cases of food-borne infection occur annually in the U.S., with death occurring in about 9,000 of these cases. Add to that the emergence of the new spongiform CJD variant, and it's obvious that trouble is rapidly heading our way.

Following WWII, and especially in recent times, Americans have developed a complacent attitude toward food. The food supply is plentiful, and for the most part is acceptable to the palate. It is perhaps this element of complacence that contributes to a feeling of security, or even invulnerability—a feeling that could be shattered by the emergence of vast populations of tiny microbes, many of which are spread by contaminated foods. For 9,000 Americans yearly, their lives are not only shattered, but abruptly ended. For tens of thousands of others, their lives are affected, some dramatically. Yet when all is said and done, it should come as no surprise that food-borne illnesses accompany animal-sourced foods, given the conditions in which the animals are raised, the source of their diet, and the treatment they receive, both physical and pharmaceutical.

Each day in the U.S., over 35 million animals are sacrificed for the benefit of the human appetite. In the time it takes to eat a chicken sandwich and a piece of lemon meringue pie (containing raw egg white that could be contaminated with *Salmonella enteritides*), the number of animals slaughtered is several times greater than the entire population of a major U.S. city such as Pittsburgh, Denver, San Francisco or Seattle. Globally, more than 45 billion animals are slaughtered for the human diet each year. For those who are mathematically challenged, this means that each year the number of animals slaughtered for food consumption is equal to nine times the Earth's human population. In time, nature balances everything. Perhaps it's payback time for the animals.

The following are some additional facts about meat consumption:[87]

♦ Almost five pounds of grain are needed to produce one pound of beef.

♦ Sixty pounds of water are needed to grow one pound of wheat. One pound of meat requires 2,500-6,000 pounds of water.

♦ According to Harvard Nutritionist Dr. Jean Mayer, reducing meat production by a mere 10% would provide enough grain to feed 60 million people.

♦ A 10-acre farm can support 60 people growing soybeans, 24 people growing wheat, 10 people growing corn and two people raising cattle.

♦ During a lifetime, the average meat eater consumes some 2,400 animals.

♦ Approximately 90,000 pounds per second (1.5 billion tons per year) of animal excrement is produced in the U.S.— some 130 times the quantity of excrement of the entire human population. This pollutes U.S. waterways more than all other sources of industrial pollution combined.

♦ More than 30% of all U.S. raw materials (including fossil fuels) are consumed in animal production.

♦ More water is consumed in U.S. beef production alone than is required to grow the nation's entire fruit and vegetable crop.

♦ To produce a single hamburger patty requires the equivalent amount of fuel to drive an automobile 20 miles, and causes five times its weight in topsoil loss.

♦ More water is saved by not eating one pound of beef than by one person not showering for a one year period.

Chapter Seven

Other Contaminants

Physical Contaminants

Contamination of modern foods occurs in yet other ways. The U.S. food supply is permitted by the FDA to contain a certain level of contamination from animal pieces or waste products. According to the FDA's published guidelines called "Food Defect Action Levels," the following levels of contamination are allowed: A seven-ounce glass of tomato juice is permitted to contain up to 25 fly eggs (maggots); a one-pound box of macaroni can have up to nine rodent hair fragments; a one-pound box of frozen broccoli can contain 276 aphids; 3.5 ounces of apple butter can have up to five whole insects; and one pound of cocoa beans can have up to 10 milligrams of rodent feces.[1] For those who enjoy eating these every-day foods, it might add a degree of mental comfort to consider these "extras" as an additional source of protein.

High-Tech Contaminants

Genetic Alteration. Just when you thought a Geo was nothing more than a cute little car, along come GEOs: Genetically

Engineered Organisms (also called GMOs, genetically modified/manufactured organisms, or simply GM; also referred to as *transgenic* organisms). Since 1993 the FDA has allowed the sale of genetically-modified foods without requiring either safety (toxicity) testing or labeling of the altered products.[2] In fact, one could safely say that a large-scale safety evaluation program of genetically-altered foods is currently being performed—on the population at large. Although no one knows the long-term results of consuming genetically-altered foods, the biotechnology industry has recently earmarked $250 million ($50 million per year for five years) for an advertising campaign to convince the public of the virtues of GM foods.

On a further discouraging note, in late January, 2002, the executive branch (European Commission) of the European Union issued a proclamation which calls for stronger backing of GM foods—a step seen as "critical to future competitiveness." The report states that ethical and environmental considerations have "distracted attention" from the strategic importance of new, biotechnological developments, including GM foods. The document suggests using "the highest standards of governance" to convince the skeptical European public of the (supposed) benefits of GM foods.

Dozens of companies including Du Pont, Eli Lilly and Monsanto (which changed its name to Pharmacia in an effort to distance itself from the bad publicity relating to genetically modified foods) are field-testing over 600 genetically-altered crops, with thousands more bacteria, insect, plant and animal combinations being planned. Some of the altered products, sometimes referred to as "Frankenfoods," include potatoes spliced with chicken genes; tomatoes spliced with fish genes; corn spliced with virus genes; and pigs spliced with human genes,[3] giving a totally new meaning to the term "designer genes."

Industry experts estimate that *at least 60% of all packaged foods, particularly those containing corn and soy, contain GMOs.* According to a study by the Union of Concerned Scientists, more than 90% of the genetic changes made to foods are related to increased profitability and ease of processing, while the remainder are focused on improving taste or nutrition.

One example of a genetically-modified food is Pharmacia's newly-developed soybean that comes complete with a built-in resistance to its own Roundup® (glyphosate), a toxic pesticide that's a major money-maker for the mega-billion-dollar agribusiness corporation. The creation of this genetically-modified soybean, called Roundup Ready,® allows for the usage of increased levels of Roundup (currently 26 million pounds world-wide each year), with no harmful effects to the beans. Monsanto/Pharmacia, nick-named the "Microsoft of microbiology," is also genetically engineering Roundup Ready corn, beets and rice, with more soon to come.

The Roundup Ready soybean presently accounts for over 70% of the total U.S. soybean crop—about 65 million acres. Monsanto plans to mix these beans with other soybean varieties, potentially (further) contaminating other soy foods such as tofu, soy milk, soy ice cream and soy-based cheese products. Currently, about 30% of corn acreage and 40% of cotton acreage is devoted to genetically-altered crops. In the years to come, citizens around the world will find themselves ingesting increasing quantities of Roundup Ready crops, if not Roundup. Industry experts estimate that more than half of biotechnology research focuses on crops that can tolerate greatly increased dosages of pesticides, a practice that could result in doubling or tripling the amount of pesticide residue in the food and water supply.

In 2001, almost half of the global soybean production was GM, along with 20% of the world's cotton, 11% of canola and seven percent of all corn. According to Agriculture News Online (www.agriculture.com), 2001 saw 130 million acres of GM crops grown in 13 countries, an increase of 19% from 2000—up 30-fold since 1996.

The potentially harmful effects of genetically-altered foods are numerous:[4] 1) formation of new toxic compounds, 2) diminished nutritional quality, 3) alteration of food composition, 4) production of new allergens, 5) diminished effectiveness of antibiotics (caused by insertion of antibiotic-resistant genes), 6) harmful side-effects of deleted genes (such as suppression of the immune system), 7) fresh appearance of old produce whose nutrients have been lost due to aging, 8) harmful effects to domestic animals, 9) harmful effects on wildlife and habitats, and 10) cross contamination of crops.

Farmers are fast discovering that GMOs don't confine themselves to the fields in which they are planted. On the contrary, many non-GMO farms, including organic farms, have been contaminated by GM seed that blows on the wind or is transported by flying creatures such as the birds and the bees. Many scientists believe this progression of cross contamination cannot be stopped. At present, hundreds of thousands of acres have been unintentionally contaminated. This has led to lawsuits and counter lawsuits by both the agribusinesses and farmers. The agribusiness view is, "The farmer used our seed. They must be held financially liable." The farmers' view is, "Agribusiness has contaminated our fields. They must be held accountable." Already, the agribusinesses have won some chilling legal decisions in the face of what seems blatantly, ethically backwards. (See www.percyschmeiser.com)

Mother Nature designed plants to produce seed so that there could be a continuous replenishing of the food supply. In their greed, the food industry has developed and patented a "terminator gene" which, once inserted, prevents any plant from producing viable seed. This eliminates the possibility of farmers saving the seed for replanting during the next season, a standard practice of farmers for thousands of years. Every year, when the farmer requires seed for his annual planting, he will have to purchase his new supply from those corporations or their affiliates that own the technology. The first company to announce this technology was Delta and Pine Land Company, along with its business partner the U.S. Department of Agriculture. As of this writing, the

USDA has completed negotiations with Delta and Pine to license and commercialize the new "terminator technology," as it is called.

Pharmacia/Monsanto's arch rival, Zeneca BioSciences (recently merged and renamed AstraZenica—although don't hold your breath, as mergers and acquisitions can occur so quickly) of the United Kingdom, is filing dozens of patent applications world wide for its own version of seed-killing technology. Dubbed "verminator technology" (because one embodiment of Zeneca's invention employs rodent genes to render seed unusable), this technology is viewed as a broader and potentially more pervasive variation in comparison to Monsanto's terminator technology. Additionally, several dozen similar patents have been issued or applied for world wide by other agrichemical corporations.

At last count, here is the tally of currently-issued patents. Holding one patent are the following: BASF (ExSeed Genetics, LLC/Iowa State University); DuPont (Pioneer Hi-Bred); Monsanto/Pharmacia; Cornell Research Foundation; and Perdue Research Foundation. Novartis holds two patents. Delta & Pine Land holds three; and Zeneca holds four. These biotechnological tools of corporate avarice and human consciousness gone haywire have the potential of altering the basic scheme of plant reproducibility—which is an integral part of nature itself. Silvia Ribeiro of the Action Group on Erosion, Technology and Concentration (ETC Group), has stated,

> The USDA's role in developing Terminator seeds is a disgraceful example of corporate welfare, involving a technology that is bad for farmers, dangerous for the environment, and disastrous for world food security.[5]

The terminator and verminator technologies are perhaps the ultimate extension of a manipulation of seed technology that has been taking place over decades. Patented, hybrid (designer) seed, for example, now dominates the market. Over a few short years, multinational corporations have bought out over 1,000 independent seed houses, businesses that had specialized in traditional

"heirloom" (open-pollinated) seed. The heirloom seed, which produce more nutritious plants that are less vulnerable to disease, is
then phased out, leaving only the patented, hybrid variety to be
sold to farmers. Hybrid seed is often "genetically tagged," a practice that prevents farmers from sharing second-generation seed
with each other. Lawsuits have been filed against farmers over
this issue.

Dozens of companies the world over are rushing to secure
their fair share of a genetically-manipulated food supply. There is
also a hectic pace of global, corporate consolidation among the
agribusiness/biotechnology companies in an effort to forge powerful alliances in this remarkable feeding frenzy to control food.
Clearly, a virtual tollbooth is being erected between the farmer
and the food. Rest assured that if these corporations had the ability to capture and meter the very air that surrounds us, we'd pay
for every breath.

The biotechnology industry has within its power the ability
to change Earth's food supply forever, or to eradicate it due to an
uncalculated oversight. In 1946, over 85% of 30 varieties of U.S.
oats, all bred from a single genetic parent, were consumed by blight.
In 1970, blight destroyed half of the U.S. corn in most southern
farming states as the result of corn being spliced with a single,
common gene. What would result if the terminator gene, as has
happened with other GM seed, infests surrounding farms, even
wild plants? Could a galloping terminator technology eventually
terminate all seed-producing plants within an entire country, or
perhaps over the entire globe? In the end, only time will tell.
However, the mere possibility of such a frightening scenario is a
major red flag signaling the need for careful monitoring of this
technology by all concerned people as well as private citizens'
groups.

An increasing number of scientists now believe that GM fish,
other marine life and insects pose at least as great a threat as GM
farm products (plants) because of their inherent mobility. According to the U.N. Food and Agriculture Organization, dozens of

different species of GM fish and other marine life have been developed, including abalone, carp, catfish, oysters and rainbow trout. The consumer groups Friends of the Earth and the Center for Food Safety have recently released a statement requesting the U.S. retail and restaurant industries neither to sell nor serve GM fish even if it were to be FDA approved at some future date.

A more in-depth treatise on genetically-engineered food can be found in Dr. Mark Lappé's 1998 book *Against The Grain: Biotechnology and the Corporate Takeover of Your Food.* Another informative book on the subject is Dr. Martin Teitel and Kimberly Wilson's *Genetically Engineered Foods: Changing the Nature of Nature (©1999).* Other useful information is available by accessing www.etcgroup.org, and www.purefood.org.

Irradiation. The first commercial use of food irradiation took place in Germany and the Soviet Union in the late 1950s. Irradiation was first used in the U.S. in 1963 when the FDA approved the irradiation of canned bacon.[6] As of 1986, the FDA has authorized its use on nearly the entire U.S. food supply. Irradiated food is exposed to ionizing radiation produced by highly radioactive isotopes such as cobalt 60 or cesium 137, or high-energy electron beams. The irradiation process inhibits ripening and destroys certain bacteria and molds that cause spoilage (although it does not kill toxins produced by bacteria during the early stages of contamination). That is to say, the shelf-life of the food is extended. Although irradiation kills most bacteria, those surviving mutate into a more resistant strain, *resistant to both irradiation and antibiotics.*

Consumption of irradiated foods has caused kidney, testicular and chromosomal damage as well as tumors in laboratory animals.[7] The consumption of irradiated rice has been linked to pituitary, thyroid, heart and lung abnormalities, and to the development of tumors. Children and laboratory animals fed irradiated wheat developed chromosomal abnormalities.[8] Studies have shown that irradiation destroys essential nutrients in food[9] including vitamins A, B_2, B_3, B_6, B_{12}, thiamine, folic acid, C, K, E, and also may produce carcinogenic compounds.[10] Amino acids and essential fatty acids (EFAs) also may be affected. A 20-80% reduction in any of the above-named nutrients is not atypical.

A group of chemicals called *cyclobutanones* is formed during the irradiation process. Cyclobutanones are not naturally-occurring substances. In fact, they do not occur anywhere on Earth except as byproducts of the irradiation process in foods such as beef, pork, chicken, lamb, mangoes, papayas, eggs, juice and sprouting seeds. These chemicals may be contributors to the health problems associated with the use of irradiation.

In a 1988 congressional hearing on the subject of irradiation, the U.S. Department of State made clear its objectives: "Promulgation of...[irradiation] technology would benefit U.S. private sector activities and minimize U.S. nuclear waste disposal problems."[11] Contrary to U.S. policy, about one-half of the member countries of the European Community do not allow extensive use of irradiation. Australia and New Zealand do not allow any use of irradiation. Irradiated whole foods were once required to be prominently labeled by the symbol of a flower within a circle. Since 1997, this symbol of governmental flower power is not required to be displayed at all. Currently, irradiated whole foods require labeling "no more prominent than required for the declaration of ingredients." There is no labeling requirement for food served in restaurants, schools, hospitals, nursing homes or other such settings. Also, labeling is not required for foods including irradiated ingredients, with the exception of foods containing irradiated meat.

Irradiating inanimate objects (food) is one thing. But consider if you will the recent ground-breaking research of John Gofman, M.D., Ph. D, clearly demonstrating a strong link between medical/dental x-rays and illness of all sorts including heart disease and cancer. Notwithstanding the catastrophic ramifications Gofman's work suggests—whatever the cost has been to the health of the public—the medical industry has been handsomely rewarded. Simply stated, Gofman believes that medical radiation has been a primary cause of cancer mortality in the United States during the past century. Medical radiation is defined, principally, as exposure to x-rays, including fluoroscopy and CT scans. Gofman believes medical radiation, received even at very low and moderate doses, is an important cause of death from Ischemic Heart Disease as well.

Dr. Gofman is a pioneer researcher who worked on the Manhattan A-bomb project in the WWII era, and is Professor Emeritus of Molecular and Cell Biology, University of California-Berkeley, which makes him a leading expert in the field of (ir)radiation. His 1999 publication, *Radiation from Medical Procedures in the Pathogenesis of Cancer and Ischemic Heart Disease: Dose-Response Studies with Physicians per 100,000 Population*, is a compendium of research including incriminating statistics spanning more than fifty years. The executive summary is available online at www.ratical.org/radiation/CNR/RMP/

Microwaves. Microwave ovens represent the zenith of American devices of convenience. In 1978, roughly 10% of American homes had microwaves. Ten years later over 65%, and now over 80% of American households zap their food with microwaves.[12] The deleterious effects of microwave radiation to human physiology and mental functioning are well known. Therefore, before microwave ovens could be placed into commerce, the industry was required to demonstrate that the dangerous waves could be contained within the confines of the oven and not adversely affect people in close proximity to the device. Even though the microwave spectrum of radiation is known to be harmful, *apparently* no thought was given as to whether the process of microwaving would cause detrimental effects to the foodstuffs themselves. Neither the government nor private industry has conducted any substantial research studies on the effects of eating microwaved foods, with the following exception.

In the early 1990s, Swiss food chemist Dr. Hans Hartel and his colleague Dr. Bernard Blanc of the Swiss Federal Institute of Technology and the University Institute for Biochemistry, carried out an experiment designed to investigate whether or not consuming microwaved foods is harmful to human health.[13] In this study, participants ate microwaved food and their blood was thereafter evaluated at various intervals for the following factors: 1) blood chemistry (iron, total cholesterol, so-called "good" HDL, and so-called "bad" LDL cholesterol), 2) hematology [erythrocytes (red blood cells), hemoglobin, mean hemoglobin concentration, mean hemoglobin content, leukocytes, and lymphocytes (white blood cells)], and 3) luminescence of bacteria.

During the first month of the study, the blood markers of those eating microwaved foods were at the "lower limits of normal." The blood analyses showed anemic tendencies, an increase in LDL cholesterol, and alteration of lymphocyte values—a pattern of degeneration characteristic of an onset of chronic and metabolic diseases such as cancer and heart disease, as Dr. Hartel explained. The results were more pronounced during the second month, and there were statistically significant differences between the microwaved and non-microwaved groups. Red blood cells, mean hemoglobin concentration and content, and HDL values decreased. LDL cholesterol and leukocytes (which increase with stress or infection) increased. There was also noted "a highly significant association between the amount of microwave energy in the test foods and the luminous power of luminescent bacteria exposed to serum from test persons who ate that [microwaved] food." Dr. Hartel concluded that a type of unnatural, technologically-derived energy may be passed along to persons eating microwaved foods—a type of energy that is not health-giving.

For his efforts toward the furtherance of science and the betterment of the human condition, lead scientist Dr. Hartel was slapped with a lawsuit brought by the Swiss Association of Dealers for Electroapparatuses for Households and Industry. The official complaint was "interfering with commerce." Dr. Hartel's accusers were victorious and the court declared that he was prohibited from communicating either in written form or in public talks that food prepared in microwave ovens is in any way dangerous to the health of the consumer. He was also ordered to pay a fine of U.S. $63,000.

In 1989, the University of Minnesota sponsored a public service radio announcement regarding the dangers of microwaving milk for babies. The announcement stated:

> Heating the bottle in the microwave can cause slight changes in the milk. In infant formulas, there may be a loss of some vitamins. In expressed breast milk, some protective properties may be destroyed...Warming a bottle...under tap water...may take a few minutes longer, but it is much safer.[14]

In 1991, an Oklahoma woman died during a non-life-threatening hip surgery after she underwent a routine transfusion with blood that had been warmed in a microwave oven.[15] It is common practice to warm blood for transfusions; however, not with microwaves. Something in the structure of the blood apparently was altered significantly enough to cause a person's death. This event was the subject of an Oklahoma lawsuit.

In April 1992, the journal *Pediatrics* published the article "Effects of Microwave Radiation on Anti-infective Factors in Human Milk."[16] The summary sentence of the abstract stated that "microwaving appears to be contraindicated at high temperatures, and questions regarding its safety exist even at low temperatures." A summary of the original research article appeared in the April 1992 issue of *Science News*, stating that microwaving breast milk "can break down not only its antibodies to infectious agents, but also its lysozymes, or bacteria-digesting enzymes," possibly causing an increased growth of more potentially pathogenic bacteria.

During the microwaving process, structures of molecules are torn apart, forcefully deformed, become impaired in quality, and cells are actually broken. This destruction and deformation at the molecular level leads to the formation of new *radiolytic* compounds not known in nature.[17]

Chapter Eight

WATER

In the United States there are roughly 26,000 industrial waste sites, at least one third of which store chemical industrial wastes in unlined pits, ponds and lagoons. It is estimated that *at least 50 billion gallons per day* of chemical waste is placed into such sites.[1] Of these thousands of sites, 7,800 are directly above ground water sources, the source of almost 50% of the nation's water supply, with no barrier separating the toxic waste from the ground water. A portion of these chemicals often seeps through the porous soil directly into the ground water. This is the same ground water used for drinking, bathing, and over 40% of the water used for crop irrigation.

A 1997 government study investigated some of these waste sites, and found organic chemical contamination of the ground water at 40 of the 50 sites investigated, and inorganic chemical contamination at 26 sites.[2] Moreover, according to a nationwide EPA survey, *9.6 billion pounds* of toxic chemicals per day are released into rivers and streams, *1.9 billion pounds* into municipal sewer systems, and *3.2 billion pounds* are injected into underground wells.[3]

The EPA lists 129 "priority" chemicals which pose a threat to human health. The actual number of hazardous chemicals is substantially higher. It is estimated there are more than 12,000 chemicals present in water, including cleansers, fertilizers, gasoline additives, metals, pesticides, radioactive substances and solvents.[4] Many of these chemicals remain in the water even after treatment by water purification methods such as chlorination and filtration. Other chemical substances also have been detected in our water supplies, including psychiatric drugs such as Prozac,® and antibiotics.[5] A 2002 study by the U.S. Geographical Survey looked at the presence of 22 antibiotics in 139 streams within a 30-state area. Forty-eight percent of the streams investigated were significantly impacted. Contamination included 14 human and veterinary antibiotics.

In addition to harmful chemicals, viral and bacterial microorganisms such as *Legionella, Giardia, Cryptosporidium, E. coli* and *Cocksackie* also pose a threat. Water-borne diseases caused by bacteria include anthrax, Asiatic cholera, brucellosis, dysentery, infectious hepatitis, paratyphoid, shigellosis, tularemia, typhoid and Weil's disease (jaundice). According to the Centers for Disease Control, 900 people die annually from drinking contaminated water, and another one million become ill.[6] According to *The New York Times*, at least one in five (20%) of Americans unknowingly drink tap water polluted with feces, radiation or other contaminants.[7]

Furthermore, there are two toxic chemicals intentionally being added to the public (tap) water supply. In numerous scientific studies, both chlorine and fluoride have been demonstrated to be toxic substances. It stands to reason the toxicity of these two chemicals would be confirmed in the scientific literature, as both chlorine and fluoride have a long history of commercial use as poisons.

Chlorine was used as a chemical weapon during WWI. Following the war, manufacturers found themselves with a huge surplus of chlorine which had been produced at great expense. The war surplus of chlorine seemed just the right ingredient to disinfect the U.S. water supply which had suffered a long history of microbial contamination. During periods of the 19th century and even into the 1920s, many large American cities were devastated by epidemics of cholera and typhoid fever, largely the result of poor sanitation of city streets—caused by horse droppings—which then contaminated the water supply.[8]

According to the EPA, approximately 75% of the U.S. population drink chlorinated tap water.[9] Chlorine or chloride is added to virtually all municipal water supplies in the U.S. for the purpose of sterilizing the water of impurities such as pathogenic bacteria. Although safe, nonchemical alternatives are available, they are generally more costly than chlorination and are therefore not implemented. Not only does chlorine sterilize the water supply, it also sterilizes the human intestinal tract, destroying the body's healthy, beneficial intestinal bacteria. Friendly intestinal flora are an important part of the body's immune system, including vitamin B_{12} production.

The drinking of chlorinated water has also been linked to an increase in colon cancer,[10] heart disease, atherosclerosis, strokes, increased levels of cholesterol, and breast and bladder cancers.[11] Bathing (including showering) in chlorinated water is also implicated due to the absorption of the chemical through the skin and respiratory tract. In fact, bathing in chlorinated water is generally considered a more potent source of contamination than drinking chlorinated water. Taking a 20-30 minute bath or shower in unfiltered water is equivalent in chlorine intake to drinking two quarts of chlorinated water.[12]

Sodium fluoride, the main source of fluoridation of the water supply, was for years the principal active ingredient in rat poison.[13] Veteran investigator Eustace Mullins quips, "Whether the adding of this compound to our drinking water is also part of a rat control program has never been publicly discussed."[14]

Fluoride was introduced into the nation's water supply following WWII. During the war, American manufacturers established the technology of manufacturing both war and domestic goods from aluminum. One difficulty associated with aluminum manufacture is the production of the byproduct fluoride. American manufacturers investigated many costly methods of disposing the toxin including burying it, dumping it into rivers, and incinerating it. In a practice reminiscent of the fertilizer and other chemical industries, a decision was made to dispose of fluoride through the municipal water supply.[15]

If these actions on the part of the monopolists (and the approval of such practices by their government lapdogs) leaves you incredulous, you have not yet understood the sheer power, brazenness and absence of morality practiced by monopoly and oligopoly transnational businesses. The facts behind the myth of fluoridation are well documented, and can be further researched by those interested in the details of the entire story. Lono A'o, in his book *Don't Drink the Water*, comments:

> ...sodium fluoride is a byproduct of aluminum manufacture, and...the transformation of sodium fluoride from dangerous chemical to benign cavity fighter came as a result of promotion from the Mellon Institute, the chief research facility of ALCOA Aluminum Company, North America's largest fluoride producer.[16]

We all enjoy the benefits of aluminum products, and probably wouldn't object to the aluminum industry using our public water supply as a convenient and inexpensive dumping ground for their industrial waste if it weren't for the simple fact that society at large is being poisoned at their convenience. The February 5, 1990 issue of *Newsweek* magazine reported that information obtained through the Freedom of Information Act showed that research pointing to health risks associated with fluoridated water was deliberately withheld from the public for many years by the U.S. Public Health Service.[17] It was, in fact, the Public Health Service that conducted the surveys which were made to appear that fluoridated water produced fewer cavities. These surveys were performed under the direction of U.S. Treasury Secretary (and oil baron) Andrew Mellon, the founder of ALCOA Aluminum.[18]

Toxic effects from fluoride have been demonstrated at levels of only 1 ppm[19] (roughly one drop in 15 gallons). Research has shown fluoride to be one of the most toxic influences to the human thyroid and endocrine system, at least in part because it is a vitamin and enzyme inhibitor. Both chlorine and fluoride are two of the most poisonous chemicals known to man.[20] At least eight reputable scientific studies have shown that fluoridated drinking water increases the risk of hip fractures by 20-40%; damages the immune system; and increases the incidence of heart disease and bone cancer in young men.[21] Fluoride in toothpaste is also potentially toxic due to its absorption through the mucus membranes of the mouth. There are many documented cases of children being poisoned from using fluoridated toothpaste.[22] But does fluoride help prevent tooth decay? Dr. Earl Mindell, America's most well-known nutritionist, comments as follows:

> I know, the common and seemingly irrefutable wisdom is that the number of cavities has been greatly decreased by the addition of fluoride to our drinking water and our toothpaste. I'm very sorry to say that it's not true, and that fluoride is most probably doing a great deal of harm.[23]

Japan has discontinued water fluoridation, as have New Zealand and Australia. West Germany banned fluoridation in 1971, the Netherlands in 1973 and most of the European Community have followed suit. To learn more about these issues, visit www.holisticmed.com/fluoride/; or www.rvi.net/~flouride/; or read Dr. John Yiamouyiannis' book *Flouride, The Aging Factor: How to Recognize and Avoid the Devastating Effects of Fluoride*.

Notwithstanding the fact that our water supply is woefully contaminated, there looms yet another challenge on the hydro horizon: water privatization. Just as the food supply has been taken over by industrial conglomerates, these same folks have their sights set on the world water supplies as well.

Scientists agree that within a relatively short time frame—by around 2025—many countries the world over will be affected by severe water shortages. Some have predicted these shortages will lead to disputes and even war between countries. In an effort to stave off this crisis, powerful organizations such as the United Nations and the World Bank, in concert with several multinational corporations, are plotting the path to our rescue.

Susan Bryce, publisher of the *Australian Freedom & Survival Guide*, sums up the issue:

> Thankfully, action has been taken—at the highest level—to avert this apocalyptic nightmare [of water shortage]. By declaring water a commodity—an economic good, to be measured, apportioned and regulated by corporations—the tide of disaster will be stemmed. This momentous decision has been made for us by a handful of transnational corporations and members of the United Nations system of organizations. This self-appointed group have mandated themselves the custodians of the world's water resources. They concede that the full-cost pricing of water, for domestic, agricultural and industrial use, will be a painful adjustment for humanity. But they argue that this is a small price to pay for water security, for their guardianship of our most precious resource.

> With the blessing of national governments, a vigorous and dynamic agenda to privatize the world's water supplies is being pursued. Traditional and indigenous rights are acknowledged, then cast aside. National sovereignty is affirmed, then eroded. Access to water—a God-given or a human right—is recognized, then suspended.

> The old economy has been fueled by oil. The new economy will be fueled by hydrodollars. A globalized trade in water is being created and we, the people, are to become the consumers in this multitrillion-dollar market.[24]

Read more about the world water crisis at www.squirrel.com.au/~sbryce; www.corpwatch.org; and www.freshwater.net/; or read Maude Barlow's book, *Blue Gold: The Global Water Crisis and the Commodification of the World's Water Supply* (available through www.ifg.org).

PART THREE:
THE SOLUTIONS

* * * * * * * *

Every problem goes through three
stages until it is recognized:
first it is made fun of
second it is contested
third it is considered obvious
—Arthur Shopenhauer (1788-1860)

Chapter Nine

THE ALTERNATIVES

Cultural Variations in Diet

Traditional cultures throughout the world avoid most of the illness and disease so characteristic of Western societies, and American society in particular. Heart disease, cancer, osteoporosis and other degenerative diseases that plague modern civilization are virtually unknown outside of developed Western cultures.

In his landmark book *Nutrition and Physical Degeneration: A Comparison of Primitive and Modern Diets and Their Effects*,[1] Dr. Weston Price makes a monumental contribution by contrasting the differences between our modern diet and that of other cultures and our ancestors. First published in 1938, this book documents the travels of Dr. Price and his wife who ventured far and wide investigating the diets of diverse groups of peoples throughout the world—14 different geographical regions in total. Dr. Price witnessed the introduction of modern foods into traditional cultures, and the devastating influences these foods have had on the indigenous populations of the various areas he studied.

He concluded that domesticated meats, cultivated rather than wild vegetables, refined flour, and sugar were particularly egregious influences in degrading the health and well-being of previously robust peoples. Dr. Price believed these modern foods are lacking in four principal nutrients: vitamins, minerals, fiber and essential fatty acids (EFAs). He concludes that the increased use of sugar and refined flour and the corresponding decrease in vitamins and minerals are the most relevant dietary changes leading to physical degeneration.

The Hunzakut of the Himalayan Mountains in northwest Pakistan is one physically remote culture where until recently the indigenous population was healthy and long-lived. Their traditional diet consisted of grains; vegetables (80% of which were eaten raw); legumes (beans and peas); and nuts and seeds. Only 1% of the total calorie intake of the Hunzakut was from animal products such as meat, milk, cheese and butter, which were used sparingly. About three ounces of meat per month were eaten, and then only on special occasions.[2]

Until recently, the people of this area lived long, and prospered. Many of the inhabitants lived in perfect health to be well over 100 years old. Several decades ago modern civilization began to encroach on the Hunzakut, and they began to consume a more "modern" diet. Since that time, their health and prosperity have declined dramatically. Other long-lived cultures of the past have met a similar fate.

During WWI, Denmark suffered a severe food shortage. Meat and white flour production were curtailed. People began to consume more whole grains, fruits and vegetables. As a consequence, the death rate in Denmark decreased by 34%. Following the war, when traditional eating habits were resumed, cancer and heart disease rose to pre-war levels.[3] During WWII, a similar pattern occurred in England, Holland, Norway and Wales. The death rate decreased following the decrease in meat consumption, and once again increased to previous levels following the war.[4] Even though the events of war are extremely stress-producing, these wartime experiences suggest that diet is even more important to good health than lack of stress.

Practical Suggestions

Processed foods and intentional additives. Become a label reader of product ingredients. If the ingredients listed on the packaging are many and polysyllabic, this should raise a concern. As Dr. Lee Hitchcox puts it: "Never eat anything you can't pronounce...or anything with a longer life expectancy than you."[5] By avoiding processed foods, especially "junk foods" such as cakes, cookies and candies, and focusing your diet on more healthy, natural foods, *you will avoid most of the harmful additives* intentionally added to the food supply.

Here are a few specifics: Regarding fats and oils, a) It's best to keep the "calories as fat" to below 30%; some recommend 20%, b) Eliminate foods containing hydrogenated oils, saturated fat and *trans* fatty acids, c) Supplement your diet with essential fatty acids such as flaxseed oil, one or two tablespoons daily. Alternatively, supplement with Dr. Udo Erasmus' Udo's Choice® Perfected Oil Blend, a blending of some eight different oils delivering the proper ratios of Omega-3, Omega-6 and Omega-9 fatty acids. This product is available in health food stores. You may visit Udo on the Web at www.udoerasmus.com, d) To prevent cooking oils from breaking down into harmful forms such as *trans* fats, the following oils can be used at high temperatures for cooking: canola; extra virgin olive; grapeseed; Malaysian red palm; or rice bran oil; and e) Avoid corn, safflower and soy as cooking oils.

Regarding sweeteners as an alternative to sugar and artificial products such as aspartame, the herbal extract *stevia* is recommended. This natural product is safe for use by diabetics, in that it does not raise blood sugar levels, and has a clean overall bill of health. The intensely-sweet herb is available from health food stores in liquid extract or powder. Learn more about it at www.dorway.com.

Other alternative sweeteners include the following:

Barley Malt. Produced by fermenting grain, the grain starches are converted into simple and complex sugars, with 40% of the final product being complex carbohydrates.

Blackstrap Molasses. The final product of the sugar-making process, blackstrap contains many of the vitamins, minerals and trace elements found in the sugar cane plant. As such, it is more nutritious than most other sweeteners.

Barbados Molasses. One of the first products produced in the sugar-making process, this product is lighter and sweeter than blackstrap due to its higher sucrose content.

Date Sugar. This type of sugar is produced from crushing dried dates, and as such is unrefined. It contains all of the nutrients and fiber found in dates.

Evaporated Cane Juice. Referred to as "unrefined sugar," this product is generally 50% less processed and contains slightly more molasses than refined sugar.

Honey. This well-known product is sweeter, contains more calories and raises the blood sugar more than refined, white sugar.

Rice Syrup. Prepared by culturing rice with enzymes and cooking to the proper consistency, rice syrup contains about 50% complex carbohydrates which produce a steady supply of energy resulting from the two to three hours required for digestion.

Unintentional additives. The best way to avoid contamination from unintentional additives—including pesticidal chemicals and other potentially harmful (and often unlabeled) ingredients such as heavy metals from fertilizers—is to eat organically-farmed produce or, alternatively, grow your own food organically. Also, since over 90% of pesticides in the American diet is the result of consuming animal products, by reducing your intake of factory-farmed animals and their byproducts such as butter, cheese, eggs and milk you will reduce your overall intake of pesticides. Confirming this is the fact that breast milk of the average nursing vegetarian mother in the U.S. contains only 1-2% of the pesticide contamination level in comparison to the national average.[6]

The term "organic" refers to foods that have been grown and processed without the use of pesticides, synthetic fertilizers, irradiation or genetic engineering. In addition, organic foods are grown in a manner that maintains the continued purity and integrity of the crop lands and water supplies. Organic farming also protects the health of farm workers and supports bio-diversity.

Some food products are labeled with terms such as "all-natural," "pesticide-free" and "residue-free." These foods are not necessarily organic. Such foods may be transported, stored or processed using chemical preservatives or other additives. To ensure you are purchasing genuine organic products, look for a label stating "certified organic."

Produce certified as organic has been grown in soil free of pesticides and synthetic chemical fertilizers for at least three years. In the case of "organic" animal farming, most states suggest cattle (beef and milk) and poultry (meat and eggs) be fed only organically-grown feed for at least one year prior to slaughter, and that the animals be free of antibiotics and growth hormones. A new national standard for organic certification of produce is currently being prepared by the USDA. There is no current organic certification program for meats.

In addition to being chemical free, organically-grown produce has been shown to contain a much higher nutrient content in comparison to conventional produce. A recent article published in the *Journal of Applied Nutrition* reported the results of a study that compares the levels of 38 minerals in organic versus conventionally-grown apples, corn, peas, potatoes and wheat. The organic foods averaged over twice the nutrient content in comparison to conventional, supermarket produce. For example, the organic foods had, on average, 63% more calcium, 78% more chromium, 73% more iodine, 59% more iron, 138% more magnesium, 125% more potassium, 60% more zinc, and 390% more of the cancer-fighting mineral selenium. At the same time, organic produce was shown to contain 40% less aluminum, 29% less lead and 25% less mercury.[7] Other studies have confirmed these results. It also has been found that the use of synthetic fertilizers and pesticides increases the nitrate content of vegetables by up to 2000%.[8]

Due to public demand as well as the entrepreneurial spirit, most American cities of any size have either a co-op or health food market that sells organic produce. Some large supermarket chains have begun to stock organic foods as well. Food stores are very sensitive to customer preferences. Ask your local grocer to stock organic products.

Meats. According to the government agencies themselves, there is virtually no way to insure that commercially-produced meats are wholesome. Even many USDA inspectors have stated the USDA seal of inspection no longer guarantees the wholesomeness or safety of the product. Cattle, poultry, swine, seafood as well as other commercially-produced animal foods have high levels of food-borne pathogen contamination. Most people don't realize that due to the high incidence of pathogenic infection, meats should be handled as if they are already contaminated, which they very likely are. One or more of the harmful microbes discussed previously can rub off on counter tops, cutting boards, knives, knife holders, hands, etc., and remain infective for some time with the potential for cross-contamination.

If you are a confirmed meat maven, the alternative to eating commercially-produced meats is to search out contaminant-free products. Many health food stores and some supermarket chains now sell meat products labeled as "natural" or "organic." The USDA has refused to institute a certification program to insure that such products are raised in a truly chemical-free environment. Therefore, it is difficult for the consumer to know the true status of the meat being purchased. In contrast, Coleman Natural Meats of Denver, CO markets genuine organic beef and lamb. Coleman is the largest producer of organic beef and lamb in the U.S., with distribution in all 50 states. Coleman's cattle graze on land untreated by pesticides and chemical fertilizers. Their organic meats are produced using no antibiotics or growth hormones, and their animals are fed only certified organically-grown feeds. To locate Coleman meats in your area, contact them at (800)442-8666.

Another source of "naturally-grown" meat is Oregon Country Beef, a cooperative of family ranchers scattered across eastern

Oregon. Meat coming from this small consortium is guaranteed to be free of growth-stimulating hormones and antibiotics. All of the animals are raised on a vegetarian diet, with none of their stock consuming animal byproducts. Their meats are not irradiated. For more information on Oregon Country Beef, contact them at (541)576-2455 or 576-2454.

Some people believe that "free range" poultry offers a healthy alternative to factory-farmed fowl. This may or may not be the case, depending on the specific conditions employed by the poultry producer. According to the USDA, the term "free range" may be used to describe fowl that have USDA-certified access to the outdoors, regardless of other conditions such as the size, composition or environmental quality of the roaming area, or the number of animals grouped together—sometimes so many that many animals have virtually no means of accessing the outdoor area. In some circumstances, the outdoor area is merely a gravel yard, with no vegetation whatsoever. In these cases, the term "free range" has no practical meaning, and the product has no practical benefit to the consumer.

Meats, including seafood and poultry, should be stored (refrigerated or frozen) and prepared (cooked) properly. To obtain specific information about the storage and cooking of meats, the USDA Meat and Poultry Hotline can provide useful information: (800)535-4555. Specialists are available during business hours (10am-4pm Eastern time) to answer food safety questions. After-hours operations offer a broad selection of safety-related recorded messages.

Animal byproducts. Most Americans are accustomed to eating a wide range of animal byproducts such as milk, cheese, butter and eggs. There are many new products available that are generally much safer than animal byproducts. Milk, butter and cheese substitutes manufactured from plant ingredients are available from health food stores (The possible caveat to this is soy-based products, because of their estrogen-like and other potentially-harmful compounds.) When shopping for such products, ensure that the ingredients are organically sourced. Otherwise, you could be eating genetically-modified or irradiated dairy substitutes.

Seafood. Because of the high level of contamination of much of the world's supply of seafood, some authorities have suggested the only seafood safe for consumption are fish caught from cold water mountain streams, and offshore ocean varieties such as cod, grouper, haddock, halibut, monkfish, ocean perch, orange roughy, pollock and snapper.[9] These varieties may be less contaminated than fish harvested from coastal waters and inland lakes and rivers; however, chemical residues have been found in offshore fish in areas as remote as Antarctica and as deep as 3,000 feet. In modern times, consuming fish is a risky business.

Antibiotics. The human digestive tract contains more bacteria than there are cells in the human body—trillions upon trillions. In a healthy human, these bacteria constitute an important line of defense against illness and disease. The indiscriminate use of antibiotics in the factory farming industry is a significant contributor to the destruction of the body's healthy population of intestinal flora.

Routine, periodic supplementation with several strains of beneficial bacteria, including *Lactobacillus acidophilus* and *Bifido bacterium*, will help maintain a healthful and proper balance of bacteria within the intestinal tract. Also, supplementing with these bacteria during and after a course of antibiotic treatment will help offset the destruction of beneficial bacteria. Both acidophilus and bifidus are available at health food stores. Most strains of these bacteria should be stored either in a refrigerator or freezer.

Water. There are at least two sources of pure drinking water: 1) certain types of bottled water, and 2) certain types of filtered water. There are many types of bottled water and many names used to describe them—distilled, spring, mountain spring, purified, drinking, sparkling, seltzer, etc. Distilled water is the preferred bottled variety for drinking. However, distilled water (as well as other types of bottled water) is subject to contamination from bacterial growth. For this reason, it's best to use a distilled water that has been bottled under ozonation—a process which helps prevent bacterial buildup. In some areas of the U.S., distilled bottled water is available that has undergone a number of treatment processes in addition to steam distillation, including reverse osmosis, deionization, submicron absolute filtration, and ozonation. This is the best variety of drinking water to search out. The International Bottled Water Association will be able to assist you in locating this preferred type of water in your area: (703)683-5213.

There is growing concern and mounting evidence that chemical plasticizers used in the manufacture of the water bottles themselves actually leach into the water. Because of this and other factors, a household filtration system may well be the safest way to ensure an uncontaminated water supply. Although many different types of filtering methods and materials for home treatment are available in today's marketplace, some products are better than others and many are totally inadequate. One preferred type of home filtration system consists of a solid block of carbon (or CBR material, a patented, particularly effective new medium) with a KDF® prefilter. The effectiveness of solid carbon as a filtering system is exemplified by the fact that one pound of this material has a surface area equivalent to six football fields.

The subject of water filtration can become quite technical, and those marketing certain types of filters may be more knowledgeable in marketing techniques than in the technical aspects of water filtration. Before purchasing a system, it would be prudent to perform due diligence. One company providing accurate technical information as well as water filtration products is Conscious Living Systems, Inc.: (888)524-8627.

An additional concern has been unearthed by Iranian physician Dr. F. Batmanghelidj. Some years ago, as a prisoner in Iran—having no access to modern medical supplies—Dr. Batman (or simply Dr. B., as he is also called) discovered the amazing healing properties of simple H_2O. According to Dr. B., much/most of human ill health is due to *dehydration*—typically defined as an abnormal depletion of body fluids. Batmanghelidj believes the incidence of dehydration is actually so high it has come to be a *normal* human condition.

"You are not sick," says Dr. B.; "you are thirsty." By rehydrating the body with copious amounts of water (along with some sea salt), Batmanghelidj has reversed such medical conditions as allergies, angina, arthritis, asthma, depression, diabetes, high blood pressure, high cholesterol, insomnia, low back pain, neck pain and obesity. For more information regarding Dr. B.'s research, read his 1995 book *Your Body's Many Cries For Water*; also, visit www.watercure.com; or call (703)848-2333.

Antidepressants. Many antidepressants work by increasing (or preventing the re-uptake of) powerful neurotransmitters, chemicals within the brain that effect our moods, eating habits, pain perception, sexual behavior, sleep habits—in short, how we think, feel and act. Chief among these is the brain's master molecule *serotonin*, denoted chemically as 5-hydroxytryptamine, or 5-HT. An adequate level of serotonin produces feelings of calmness and relaxation. A low level produces the opposite—depression, anxiety, insomnia, and other negative feelings and behaviors.

Because of the harmful effects experienced by so many users of SSRI and similar pharmaceutical antidepressants, it's best to avoid them in favor of several more natural alternatives. (It's important to note, however, that the use of SSRIs should never be stopped immediately, and any SSRI should be allowed to clear from the body before other products are taken.) Alternative medical practitioner Dr. Julian Whitaker, writing in his excellent (and strongly-recommended) newsletter *Health & Healing: Tomorrow's Medicine Today* (www.drwhitaker.com; 800/539-8219), recommends three effective products in treating mild to moderate depression:

1) *5-hydroxytryptophan (5-HTP)*. Even a novice at chemistry will notice that 5-HTP has a very close chemical formula to that of the brain's master molecule 5-HT, serotonin. Used medicinally, 5-HTP is not a synthetic drug, but rather an extract

from the African plant *Griffonia simplicifolia* (perhaps even in its name trying to suggest that we row the boat slowly). 5-HTP is a precursor of serotonin, i.e., it provides the building materials out of which the body makes serotonin.

By increasing 5-HTP—which has direct and rapid access through the blood-brain barrier directly to the brain—serotonin levels are also increased. Levels of other neurotransmitters also are raised by 5-HTP, including dopamine, melatonin and norepinephrine. 5-HTP has been approved in Europe for decades as a treatment for many medical complaints including anxiety, depression, insomnia and weight loss. Medical practitioner and author Dr. Michael Murray has used 5-HTP with hundreds of patients, and reports tremendous results, including mood elevation, increased vitality and energy levels—a basic rediscovery of the joys of being alive. To learn more about the benefits of 5-HTP, read Dr. Murray's 1998 book, *5-HTP: The Natural Way to Overcome Depression, Obesity, and Insomnia.*

2) *St. John's Wort.* Known botanically as *Hypericum perforatum*, the herb St. John's Wort has been used for centuries to treat a variety of both physical and mental disorders. It was used during the Crusades as a battlefield antiseptic. Disorders of mood and temperament have been treated successfully by St. John's Wort for centuries. Its antidepressant and mood stabilizing qualities result from its principal active ingredient, the compound *hypericin.*

A study of more than 1700 patients comparing St. John's Wort to pharmaceutical antidepressants was reported in the *British Medical Journal* in August, 1996.[10] Hypericum extract was found to be at least as effective as pharmaceutical drugs in treating mild to moderate depression, while having about half the number of reported side effects. Almost twice the number of participants taking standard antidepressants dropped out of the study due to side effects in comparison to the Hypericum group. Many other studies report similar results.

In Germany, extracts of St. John's wort are approved for the treatment of anxiety, depression and sleep disorders. The herb is considered quite safe when taken as directed, although it may cause sun/skin sensitivity in some individuals. Also, St John's Wort interacts with Coumadin,® digoxin, theophylline, oral contraceptives, transplant (antirejection) drugs, and several AIDS medications, according to Dr. Whitaker.

3) *S-adenosyl-methionine* (SAM-e; pronounced "sammy"). SAM-e is produced from two substances normally found within the body—*methionine* and *adenosine triphosphate* (ATP). (Methionine is an amino acid; ATP is manufactured within the cells, and provides the energy to fuel the body's processes.) SAM-e works by elevating the brain's serotonin levels and balancing other neurotransmitters.

Seventy percent of depressed persons taking SAM-e notice mood improvement within days, as opposed to pharmaceutical antidepressants that typically require from two to four weeks to take effect (and then, the effects can be devastating). Dr Richard Brown, associate professor of clinical psychiatry at Columbia University and co-author of the 1999 book *Stop Depression Now*, describes SAM-e as the breakthrough supplement that works as well as prescription drugs, in half the time, with no side effects.

Chapter Ten

SUPER SUPPLEMENTS

A poor diet—causing one to be *mal*nourished—is one possible cause of suppressed immune function. When the body doesn't receive the proper fuel, it simply cannot function properly. Garbage in, garbage out, as they say. Obviously, the most advantageous means of maintaining a healthy immune system would include a proper diet complete with all of the nutrients the body requires.

For those who find themselves with a compromised immune system, regardless of the reason(s), an extra immune boost may be desirable—not as a dietary substitute, but as a supplement, an adjunct. Recently, several powerful immune-boosting products have come to the marketplace.

In addition, antimicrobials are another type of supplement that many may find beneficial. Poor eating habits leave the body susceptible to invaders such as harmful bacteria, viruses, fungi and parasites. Several new, "natural" antimicrobials will be discussed.

Immune Boosters

The human immune system is the body's first line of defense against all forms of illness. The lymphatic system, liver, spleen, thymus and bone marrow interrelate in the immune systems normal defense strategies. The tonsils, appendix and Peyer's patches (lymphoid tissues within the small intestine) are also related to immune function; and there are no doubt many other as-of-yet unknown nuances of the rather miraculous human immune system. A healthy immune system is able to ward off most challenges by infecting microbes such as viruses, bacteria, fungi, yeast, parasites and a host of toxic substances. However, those with a suppressed immune function such as the infirm, elderly and the very young are at higher risk.

IP$_6$.[1] One new immune-boosting product is IP$_6$, *inositol hexaphosphate.* Inositol is a member of the B-complex family of vitamins, and IP$_6$ is formed by the addition of six phosphate groups (which involves atoms of the mineral phosphorous). IP$_6$ is a component of fiber, and is found principally in whole grains and legumes. The inositol component in foods, however, is not easily absorbed and utilized.

IP$_6$ has been shown to be a powerful immune booster due in part to its ability to increase the activity of "natural killer" (NK) cells, one of many types of white blood cells—the cellular mediators of immunity. NK cells attack and destroy viruses, bacteria, parasites and other microbial sources of infection. IP$_6$ is also an effective antioxidant, protecting cells from damaging free radicals. Additionally, it has been shown to be effective in both preventing and treating certain types of cancers, including brain, breast, colon, fibroblast, leukemia, liver, prostate, skeletal muscle sarcoma and skin cancers. It appears that IP$_6$'s principal mode of action is in controlling cell division. It signals the cancer cells to stop dividing and stop producing DNA. Unlike more traditional cancer treatments such as chemotherapy, which indiscriminately kill both beneficial and harmful cells, IP_6 attacks only the cancerous cells.

IP_6 is more potent when combined with inositol at a ratio of 4:1 IP_6 to inositol. The patented product Cell Forté, marketed by Enzymatic Therapy, combines IP_6 and inositol at this optimal ratio. Otherwise, any brand could be used in a combination of these two ingredients at the recommended ratio. In both animal and human testing, no side effects have been observed even at higher dosages. IP_6 is available from your local health food store. More information can be obtained from Dr. AbulKalam Shamsuddin's book *IP_6: Nature's Revolutionary Cancer-Fighter* (©1998); also available is *The IP_6 with Inositol Question and Answer Book* (©1999), by L. Stephan Coles, M.D., Ph. D., et al.

Beta-1,3-D-Glucan:[2] Referred to simply as *beta glucan*, this product is a simple polysaccharide (sugar/carbohydrate) that typically is extracted from the cell wall of baker's and brewer's yeasts, and oats (although the yeast products do not contain any yeast proteins that cause allergic reactions). In the 1980s, Harvard University's Joyce Czop, Ph. D, discovered that beta-1,3-glucan matches a receptor site (a lock-and-key type of arrangement) on the surface of *macrophages*, a critical component of the immune system. When beta glucan links to macrophages, they become activated.

Macrophage literally means "big eater," and is so named because these cells circulate throughout the body engulfing and consuming toxins and debris including viruses, bacteria, fungi and parasites. They perform a critical role in the initiation and maintenance of the immune response. The entire immune system becomes mobilized when macrophages are activated. Macrophages also assist T-cells, another type of immune defender cell, in recognizing and destroying foreign substances. NK cells are also stimulated.

In animal studies, beta glucan has been demonstrated effective in treating many ailments, including malignant melanoma, skin ulcers, leukemia, viral hepatitis, wound healing and in killing *E.*

Coli bacteria. In the mid-1980s, the first human testing with (advanced) HIV/AIDS was done. Beta glucan increased immune activity even in these advanced patients. Other human studies also have been done. One such study was conducted by Dr. Peter Mansell of the McGill University Cancer Research Unit. Dr. Mansell found beta glucan to be an effective treatment of malignant lesions in both animals and humans. He observed either complete or partial resolution of 100% of the human lesions when injected intralesionally.

Interestingly, beta glucan taken orally has been shown to offer protection against radiation. The United States Armed Forces Radiobiology Institute found that when rats were given a lethal dose of radiation, 70% of the animals suffered no ill effects when beta glucan was given orally *following the radiation exposure*. These findings suggest beta glucan might be applicable as a preventive against harmful radiation at the time of exposure to medical/dental x-rays, for example, or in the case of a radiation accident, or worse.

Researchers believe it is specifically the 1,3 molecule that causes the strongest immune response. Therefore, those looking for immune support should focus on beta 1,3 versus 1,4 and 1,6. There are no known side effects caused from using beta glucan, and no known prescription or over-the-counter (OTC) drug interactions, other than its potentiating effect on antibiotics, antimicrobials and cholesterol-lowering drugs. This product is available from your local health food store. More information is available in Dr. Leonid Ber's 1998 book, *Activate Your Immune System*, or Roger Mason's 2001 booklet, *What is Beta Glucan?*

MGN-3 (Arabinoxylane Compound, U.S. Patent 5,560,914). MGN-3 is produced by hydrolyzing rice bran with the enzymatic extract of shiitake mushrooms. According to the manufacturer, this combination improves systemic absorption, thereby increasing its immune-enhancing properties. The principal means of MGN-3's effectiveness is its ability to increase NK cell activity. At least nine clinical efficacy studies have shown NK cell activity increased by more than 300%; B-cell activity increased by 250%; and T-cell activity increased by 200%.

MGN-3 has no known side effects, and has no dangerous interactions with either prescription or OTC drugs. It is available from health food stores, or by calling LaneLabs at (800)526-3005; or visit www.lanelabs.com.

Hydroxygen Plus. One relatively new product gaining recognition and popularity is Hydroxygen Plus, manufactured exclusively by Global Health Trax of Poway, CA. Consisting of a proprietary blend of natural (vegetarian) ingredients, this product is a powerful blood (cellular) oxygenator. It also supplies hydrogen, and a full spectrum of minerals, amino acids and enzymes.

By increasing the oxygen content of the blood, the cells become more nourished and the waste elimination process is made more efficient. When cells become burdened with a buildup of toxic substances, it is only logical that health begins to fail. When the body's trillions of cells are functioning at an optimal level, so too is the immune system able to offer peak performance.

It is well known that microorganisms beneficial to the body, as well as normal cellular structures, thrive in an oxygen-rich (aerobic) environment. Conversely, most harmful organisms such as viruses, bacteria, fungi and parasites—as well as abnormal cells such as cancers—thrive in a low-oxygen (anaerobic) environment, and cannot survive in a highly oxygenated environment. Two-time Nobel Laureate Dr. Otto Warburg stated that although there can be many secondary causes of cancer, there is only one primary cause: "...replacement of the normal oxygen respiration of body cells by an anaerobic cell respiration."

Recognizing the importance of highly-oxygenated blood all the way down to the cellular level, it is understandable that Hydroxygen is producing dramatic results in response to a wide variety of medical problems, from minor ailments to serious medical conditions.

Medical investigative journalist Ed McCabe, author of the best-seller *Oxygen Therapies: A New Way of Approaching Dis-*

ease, believes Hydroxygen to be the best product of its type on the market. Writing about the product, McCabe uses the words "astonishing," "amazing," and "miracle results" to describe Hydroxygen. Mr. McCabe's latest book, *Flood Your Body With Oxygen: Therapy for Our Polluted World* (©2002), gives a glowing review of this product. To learn more about Hydroxygen, visit www.globalhealthtrax.org/21107

Antimicrobials

The words *antimicrobial* and *antibiotic* are roughly interchangeable. They are substances that prevent, inhibit or destroy life—in this case, microbes. However, as discussed in Chapter Five, the pharmaceutical antibiotics presently in use today are facing a crisis of major proportion due to the antibiotic-resistant microbes that now resist treatment by virtually all of modern medicines' germ-killing arsenal. Even at the height of their effectiveness, pharmaceutical antibiotics were primarily anti*bacterial*; they never have been an effective treatment against many other types of microbes, such as viruses.

Within the last few years, several "natural" preparations have come to market that are truly broad spectrum in their application. These products are not only effective against bacteria, but a host of other malingering microbes such as viruses, fungi, yeasts and many varieties of parasites. Although these products are labeled as antimicrobials, they also provide a boost to the immune system. Destruction of harmful microbes that systemically infect the body relieves the immune system of a great burden.

Grapefruit Seed Extract.[3] A complicated, bio-technological process is used to extract the active ingredients of this product from the seeds and pulp of common grapefruit. The extract is chemically identified as a *diphenol hydroxybenzene complex*, and contains primarily bioflavonoids, glycosides and several proteins. Research into the properties and effectiveness of this potent extract spans more than two decades, although most of the research has taken place within the last ten years by such prestigious institutions as the Pasteur Institute (France); the Institute for Microecology (Germany); the University of Sao Paulo (Brazil); the U.S. Department of Agriculture; the University of Georgia, and scores of others. Grapefruit seed extract has been demonstrated effective against more than 800 bacterial and viral strains, 100 strains of fungi and yeasts, as well as a significant number of single- and multi-celled parasites.

In terms of its bactericidal properties, grapefruit seed extract is effective against such heavy hitters as *Campylobacter jejuni, Chlamydia trachomatis, Clostridium botulinum, Giardia lamblia, Helicobacter pylori, Mycobacterium tuberculosis, Pseudomonas aeruginosa, Salmonella enteritides, Staphylococcus aureas, Streptococcus faecalis, Trichomonas vaginalis,* and hundreds of additional gram-positive and gram-negative bacteria. One recent, published study found grapefruit seed extract effective against 249 strains of *Staphylococcus aureas*, 86 strains of Streptococcus, 232 strains of Enterococcus, 77 strains of Enterobacter, 86 strains of *E. Coli*, 22 strains of Klebsiella, and 18 species of Proteus.

As a virucide, it has been shown effective against *Influenza A$_2$, Herpes simplex Type 1*, and *Measles virus morbillium*. Grapefruit seed extract is also used as an adjunct for immune support and to guard against infection in chronic immunodeficiency diseases such as AIDS, chronic fatigue syndrome and Candida. As a fungicide, it has shown effectiveness against 71 varieties of fungal yeast and 22 varieties of fungal mold.

Many medical practitioners believe that parasitic infection represents a primary, underlying cause of illness and disease of which most people, including physicians, are not aware. Parasites are a significant problem in today's world, even in first-world countries such as the U.S. Of the more than 130 varieties of parasites that can use humans as their hosts, many Americans harbor at least one. In 1976, the U.S. Centers for Disease Control conducted a random sampling of the entire population. One out of every six people was infested with at least one type of parasite. Some physicians estimate that 50-80% of their patients are infected. Medical researchers have estimated that 50% of all Americans will suffer from some type of parasitic infection during their lifetimes.

Parasitic invaders generally reside in the digestive tract, blood, and the lymphatic system, and their effects can be quite broad. Any type of parasitic infection can be devastating to the immune system. Symptoms can include apathy, anxiety, arthritis, depression, fatigue, food allergies, lack of concentration, poor memory, rashes, swelling, and many others. More serious maladies often result. For example, AIDS researchers at the University of Virginia discovered that the simple (single-celled) amoeba can produce a substance that disrupts the structure of the immune defense cells that surround and deactivate the HIV virus. Untreated, the virus can multiply without restraint. Some researchers believe such maladies as Alzheimer's, diabetes, and Hodgkin's disease can be attributed to parasitic infection. It is comforting to know that grapefruit seed extract is effective against a wide variety of parasites. In humans, the extract has been tested successfully against microscopic parasites. In animal studies, the extract has shown clear effects on larger organisms.

According to the literature, grapefruit seed extract is nontoxic even when taken in high dosages. More than 4,000 times the normal dose would be necessary to be life-threatening. Beneficial intestinal lactobacilli are only slightly affected by the extract, and *Bifidobacteria* are totally unaffected. Grapefruit seed extract is considered hypoallergenic, with the possible exception of 3-5% of the population who are allergic to citrus fruit, and could display a sensitivity. In the U.S., it is an FDA GRAS-listed (Generally Recognized As Safe) substance.

One interesting property of grapefruit seed extract is that it has been tested non-toxic when used as an inhalant. In one test, subjects were subjected to a concentration of 100-150 mg of grapefruit seed extract per cubic meter of air, eight hours a day, five days a week for 90 days. No negative health effects were noted. The significance of this lies in the fact that grapefruit seed extract might have an application as an anti-biological (germ) warfare agent. For example, the bacterium anthrax (*Bacillus anthracis*) is widely feared as a deadly biological agent. When the spore-forming bacterium enters the lungs there is little hope. Because grapefruit seed extract is bacteriacidal to so many varieties of bacteria, it could be possible that this extract is effective against *Bacillus anthracis*—especially in its cutaneous form. Even if it were bacteriostatic (diminishes, but does not completely kill), it could provide enough time for additional antibiotics to act through the blood stream. Further testing of the substance would be required before any definite conclusions could be drawn.

Several brand names appear in health food stores, Citricidal® being one of the most potent. Citricidal contains a standardized extract of 60% grapefruit seeds in a 40% solution of vegetable glycerine. Another brand is GSE,® marketed by NutriBiotic.® GSE contains 33% Citricidal and 67% vegetable glycerine. A powdered product is also available (in tablets and capsules). Follow dosage recommendations on the product labeling. More information is available in Sharamom and Baginski's 1995 book *The Healing Power of Grapefruit Seed.*

Olive Leaf Extract. An old cure has recently been rediscovered—from the leaves of the common olive tree, botanically classified as *Olea europaea L.* Documentation of the effective medicinal uses of the olive tree dates back some 6,000 years. In the *Bible*, the olive tree is called "the tree of life." Over this long span of time, various parts of the tree have been used medicinally. Olive oil, for example, was used by Hippocrates as a cure for cholera, muscular pains and ulcers. The leaves of the tree have been used as a medicinal tea for centuries, although this remedy has been practically unknown to modern, Western medicine—until only recently.

During the years 1827-1855, there were reports in the medical literature of olive leaves being used to brew a tea which was believed to be a potential cure for malaria. Later that century, biochemical analyses were performed on powdered olive leaves, and an active ingredient was isolated and given the Latin name *oleuropein* ($C^{25}H^{32}O^{13}$). By 1969, researchers at the pharmaceutical giant The Upjohn Company had done further analyses of oleuropein and found the principal ingredient to be a calcium salt of elenolic acid, which is chemically identified as *calcium elenolate*, a chemical byproduct of oleuropein.

The studies performed by Upjohn found that olive leaf extract—calcium elenolate—inhibited the growth of every virus, bacterium, fungus, yeast and parasitic protozoon it was tested against. The pharmaceutical firm intended to patent the extract and market it as a drug. They abandoned their efforts, however, after finding that calcium elenolate binds to proteins in blood serum, rendering it ineffective as a treatment. By the mid-1990s, other researchers discovered a remedy to this obstacle, thus opening the door for the extract's use as an antimicrobial nutritional supplement.

In his book *Olive Leaf Extract*,[4] Morton Walker, M.D. reports many seemingly miraculous benefits of this substance:

♦ the generalized degradation of pathological microorganisms of all types—viruses, retroviruses, bacteria, spirochetes, rickettsiae, chlamydiae, fungi, yeasts, molds, protozoa, helminths, and other parasites

♦ the relief of arthritic inflammations, especially osteoarthritis and rheumatoid arthritis

♦ the reduction of insulin dosage for better control over the risks of symptomatic diabetes

♦ the elimination of chronic fatigue and the symptoms associated with its syndrome

♦ the creation or restoration of abundant energy with prolonged stamina

♦ the normalization of heart beat irregularities (arrhythmias)

♦ the improvement of blood flow in cardiovascular and/or peripheral vascular disorders

♦ the lessening of pain from hemorrhoids

♦ the attenuation of toothaches

♦ the antioxidant quenching of free radical pathology

♦ the obliteration of fungal infections such as mycotic nails, athlete's foot, and jock itch

♦ the permanent relief of malaria (from a protozoa), dengue fever (from a virus), and other exotic and deadly tropical diseases which produce fever as a primary symptom

♦ the prevention and effective treatment of all types of viral diseases, including the Epstein-Barr virus, cytomegalovirus, the herpes viruses, human herpes virus-6, the retroviruses, the influenza viruses, viruses of the common cold, and the human immunodeficiency virus (HIV)

♦ the reversal of almost all symptomatology connected with Candida albicans and other organisms causing the yeast syndrome

♦ the death and excretion of a variety of parasites, including microscopic protozoa and macroscopic helminth worms

Dr. Walker describes the above as a *partial* list of the benefits provided by oral administration of olive leaf extract! This powerful germ fighter is not only effective, but safe. In 1969, The Upjohn Company conducted a battery of tests to determine the exact toxicity of calcium elenolate. The tests were performed on a variety of laboratory animals, and showed the substance to be "exceedingly safe and non-toxic."

Calcium elenolate also has been used successfully in an intranasal spray containing up to 2% calcium elenolate. Could it be that the olive branch, the United Nations' international symbol of peace, is able to defeat an enemy such as anthrax? Dr. Walker's book cites a list of more than 125 infectious diseases for which olive leaf extract acts as an antimicrobial agent—as determined by Upjohn and others. On this list, anthrax appears third from the top (probably the cutaneous, not the inhaled, variety)—just under AIDS and amoebiasis. The list is impressive, and its veracity is documented by over 25 published studies spanning more than four decades.

Ranging from AIDS to Yellow fever, some of the list-entrants include athlete's foot, chicken pox, chlamydia, cholera, colds, crabs, diarrhea, diphtheria, ebola Sudan, ebola Zaire, E. coli O157:H7, Epstein-Barr, gonorrhea, herpes, hepatitis A/B/C, leprosy, lockjaw, Lyme disease, malaria, measles, mumps, pneumonia, polio, rabies, scarlet fever, smallpox, syphilis, tuberculosis, typhoid fever, warts, whooping cough, and almost 100 others.

Your local health food store carries a selection of olive leaf extract products in a variety of strengths, in either tablets or capsules. Dr. Walker recommends an oleuropein concentration of greater than 6%. Some products contain as much as 15%, or higher. Follow dosage directions on the product labeling.

Oil of Oregano.[5] The oil from the oregano plant is yet another ancient medication only recently rediscovered. The first recorded medicinal use of the oil was by the Assyrians over 5,000 years ago, circa 3,000 B.C. Few realize the plant was known as Bible hyssop. For hundreds of years, the ancient Greeks and Romans used oregano medicinally as well. Greek physicians used it to treat headaches, lung disorders, open wounds, seizures, venomous bites, and narcotic poisoning. In fact, if someone had slipped Socrates some oil of oregano or perhaps some oregano tea, he may have lived to anger the village elders yet another day. The Greeks regarded oregano as the definitive cure for hemlock poisoning.

Medicinal oil of oregano is the essential oil of only a select few species of the more than 40 oregano and oregano-like species in existence today. The medicinal varieties are not the same species found in the spice section of your local herb market, and not the same as that used on pizza. The product is produced by steam distillation of the crushed flowers and leaves of only select varieties of wild oregano plants. The principal active ingredient is *carvacrol*, a phenolic compound present in the flowers and leaves. Another phenol, *thymol*, is the second most active compound, although it is present at less than 1%.

For much of the 20th Century—as late as the 1950s—the synthetic phenolic compound *carbolic acid* was the primary antiseptic (antimicrobial) used on hospital patients and by physicians to sterilize surgical equipment—the standard against which all other antiseptics were measured. Carvacrol is even more potent than carbolic acid as an antiseptic. According to Dr. Cass Ingram, as reported in his book *The Cure Is In The Cupboard*, oil of oregano is the Rolls Royce of all natural antiseptics—meaning that it is an effective, broad-spectrum antimicrobial, including antiviral, antibacterial, antifungal and anti-parasitic action.

Dr. Ingram also makes a strong case for oil of oregano as an anti-inflammatory, antioxidant, and anti-venom agent capable of neutralizing the toxic effects of ants, bees, scorpions, snakes and spiders. It is also a mucolytic (mobilizes mucus), an antitussive (halts coughs), and an antispasmodic (eases muscle tightness and spasms).

Oil of oregano is active in small amounts when taken internally. It is also effective as a topical antimicrobial. Medicinal oregano is also available as a powdered herb in capsules. It is recommended that only products with at least a 55% carvacrol content be used. At least two such products are available from health food stores, one from North American Herb and Spice, the other from Nature's Answer.

Chapter Eleven

CONCLUSIONS

I t seems obvious to say that changes must come to those structures, both private and public, that have brought our problemed
food supply into being, and allow it to continue to prosper.
Change on this level, however, is often a long-termed and labori-
ous process. Only time will reveal the ultimate outcome of the
power politics of food production—and the world of big business
and even bigger money.

The outcome of many human issues and events presently remains shrouded in uncertainty. The conclusions are pending—the
final act is as yet unwritten. That having been said, as this book is
being prepared for publication, Manhattan has just lost a sizable
portion of its most prized real estate. Powerful forces are at play
in matters of war, peace and food alike, as General Butler discovered. We live during interesting times.

No matter what is to be our destiny as a nation or a planet, on
an individual level the results of our actions are more discernable,
more easily seen. Practically speaking, for ourselves, we can make
wise choices in the marketplace that affect our individual health
as adults, and our families. Personal dietary choices represent one

area over which most people, especially within the Western world, can exercise a significant amount of influence—at least if we are aware of the issues, and some reasonable answers.

As we have seen, many of the corporations that produce the foods for our consumption are obviously more concerned about issues other than margins of safety. The government agencies whose duty it is to oversee food safety cater to the concerns of big business rather than the safety of the people who pay the salaries of these public guardians. With this in mind, it should be understood that few are watching out for the consumer other than the consumer him/herself. Caveat emptor—let the buyer beware! This is the only way a consumer will avoid becoming an unknowing pawn and victim of corporate negligence and avarice.

It is important to understand that the unfortunate circumstances surrounding Earth's contaminated food supply represent a mere microcosm in comparison to the larger story presently unfolding around the globe. Virtually all other areas of commerce and industry are being affected similarly—the same forces are at play. From the alpha to the omega, from birth to death, modern man is being absorbed into a corporate infrastructure which by its very nature tends to push humanity in the direction of inhumanity.

How and when will this situation be corrected? Changes will come only when enough people become aware, and act on that awareness by expressing their preferences with their purchasing power, in the voting booth and in other conscious and deliberate ways. Knowledge is powerful, and so are the actions and pocketbooks of consumers.

On a practical level, if large numbers of consumers voice their opinions through their purchasing practices, the corporate food monopolies would be more inclined to alter their questionable behavior. If consumers demonstrate their preferences by avoiding processed foods, produce, and meats produced through the use of harmful chemicals, the food giants—who are desirous of selling their products—would be more apt to offer a wholesome array of nutritious foods. By purchasing more healthful foods you are not only helping yourself, but also registering your dissatisfaction with contaminated foods and letting your voice be heard.

One recent victory of the people over their corporate/government overseers demonstrates the power and effectiveness of concerned citizens. In early 2002, pharmaceutical industry executives and politicians representing more than 50 countries met in Berlin, Germany under the auspices of the United Nation's "Codex Alimentarius" Commission. The main purpose of this meeting was to establish global legislation intended to restrict access to nutritional supplements and other natural health therapies. The Commission's plan was met with a world-wide public outcry of protest. Over 100 million protest letters and emails were sent by people from around the world to both politicians and the members of the "Codex" Commission. While the demand from over 100 million protest letters stopped the pharmaceutical industry's strategies at the level of Codex Alimentarius, similar efforts continue at the level of the EU-Commission and the European parliament. Citizens must be ever vigilant regarding all of our rights and freedoms.

Nothing could be more true than in the area of food production. The consumer must be continually alert regarding the condition of the food supply, as the food producers are ever on the march to increase their revenues, and apparently will let no obstacle stand in their way. One of the latest tricks up their collective sleeves is to alter the definition of the term "organic" to include foods that have been irradiated and genetically altered. In fact, in 1977 the USDA sought to change the law to include GM foods within the definition of "organic." In another demonstration of the power of concerned and informed citizens, nearly 300,000 letters of protest forced the USDA to rewrite their proposal.

Another notch on the gun belt of the food monopolies, as mentioned, is the Agricultural Product Disparagement Laws—the recent legislation which gave the food industry unprecedented power to bring lawsuits against people critical of their products. This powerful tool can be used in an attempt to silence food-safety activists and environmentalists from speaking out about these important issues. To date, 13 states have enacted such a law, with another 14 states contemplating a similar law. Oprah Winfrey's acquittal signals new hope for the consumer. Some activist groups believe that Winfrey's successful defense of her right to free speech could serve to dull the teeth of such laws of prohibition.

Yet one more tactic is currently being used by the mega-corporations, a tactic referred to as *greenwashing*—a polite term for *whitewashing*, but done under the guise of being friendly to the environment, and the people. Although there are many forms of greenwashing, one form may eventually turn out to be the corporate takeover of the organic food market, with a possible future reversion to its previous state. Remember, these are business concerns in posession of vast sums of money, enough to purchase *anything*, including true "green" businesses that have been built by conscientious people. Then, for whatever reasons, the green businesses sell out to the multinationals. The important question is whether or not these bought-out businesses will continue to produce a wholesome product as envisioned and practiced by their originators—or, over time, whether they will be degraded to the extent that they are totally subverted. Time will tell, although past experience doesn't inspire confidence. (Learn more by reading Kenny Bruno and Jed Greer's 1996 book, *Greenwash: The Reality Behind Corporate Environmentalism*.)

For you personally, one of two choices must be made regarding the contaminated food supply and the foods you eat. Each choice differs from the other as night from day. The two choices are: "ignorance is bliss" (and its side-kick "what you don't know won't hurt you"), versus "informed consumerism." You must decide for yourself what position to take. You can turn your head and look the other way, or attempt to protect yourself and your family from a contaminated food supply. It's your choice. No one can make the decision for you and if you *do* confront the problem, it *does* involve some effort. If you choose to look the other way, don't expect the bliss to follow automatically because in this instance, what you eat can kill you—even if it takes a few years.

When exercising your dietary choices, remember the seriousness of the unhealthy consequences of making uninformed and unconscious decisions. For the most part, these consequences are long-term and unforgiving. Even though change is sometimes difficult—as they say, "old habits die hard"—it's much more preferable that the habits die rather than you.

Change needn't occur all at once—in a day, a week or a month. If you are guided from a point of understanding, change will seep into your lifestyle and occupy the status of newer, more healthy habits that began only as the smallest of understandings. If you learn to be discriminating in your eating habits, you will increase your chances of living a life free of illness and disease.

Although it has taken the better part of 100 years for the food giants to sneak up on the unsuspecting, many have not yet understood the issues surrounding the contaminated food supply. However, some progress has been made. Especially within the European Community, people are beginning to wake up to some of the dangers—particularly the dangers of genetically-modified foods and hormone-laden meats. The understanding of the American public still lags behind, and needs to grow.

On a global level, Earth is hurting for a change, and there's little time to waste. Many segments of humanity are heading in directions that threaten all of human life. And, as the ancient Chinese proverb smugly tells us, "If we keep proceeding in the same direction, surely we will end up where we are heading." If people fail to understand the important issues facing humanity today—*if people fail to come to their own rescue*—it may come to pass that all the king's horses and all the king's men can't put Earth, Inc. back together again. If this were to happen, where would we go? What would we do? Will humanity go so far as to cut off the branch on which it is sitting? Or will we heed the inspired slogan that has adorned T-shirts and trinkets alike, "Good Planets Are Hard To Find."

NOTES

Chapter 1: The Framework
1. University of Texas Eisenhower Archives: www.eisenhower.utexas.edu/farewell.htm
2. Marine Corps University Archives: www.mcu.usmc.mil/MCRCweb/smedley.htm
Butler, Smedley, D. *War Is A Racket*. Noontide Press: Costa Mesa, CA, 5ᵗʰ printing, 1991.
3. Marrs, Jim. *Rule By Secrecy*. Harper-Collins Publishers, Inc.: New York, NY, 2000, p. 46.
4. "Standard Oil Company and Trust." *The New Encyclopedia Britannica*. Vol. II, 15ᵗʰ edition, 1998, pp. 207-208.
5. Longman, Phillip, J. and Egan, Jack. "Why Big Oil is Getting a lot Bigger." *U.S. News & World Report*, Dec. 14, 1998, p. 26.
6. Cockburn, Alexander, and St. Clair, Jeffrey. "Food Central: How Three Firms Came to Rule the World." www.counterpunch.org/food.html.
7. Ibid.
8. Ibid.
9. As per note 2.

Chapter 2: The Betrayal
1. *Essex County, New Jersey, Medical Society Bulletin, 1967.* [Cited in Winter, 1991, as per note 2, p. 8.]
2. Winter, Ruth, M.S. *Poisons in Your Food*. Crown Publishers, Inc.: New York, NY, 1991, p. 3.

3. *U.S. News & World Report.* November, 24, 1997.
4. Larrick, George. "The Consumer Looks at Chemicals in Our Food." *Food, Drug and Cosmetic Law Journal*. Vol. 12, No. 6, June 1957, p. 345.
5. Lyons, R. "Trouble Over Drugs on the Market." *The New York Times*. Jan. 4, 1970, pp. 4-5.
6. Young, Frank E., M.D., Ph. D. "FDA's Year of Foods," *An FDA Consumer Special Report, Safety First: Protecting America's Food Supply.* 1988.
7. Carter, James, M.D., Dr. P.H. *Racketeering in Medicine: The Suppression of Alternatives*. Hampton Roads Publishing Co., Inc.: Charlottesville, VA, 1993, p. 170, ©1993 Hampton Roads Publishing Co., Inc. All rights reserved. Quotation reprinted by permission.
8. Jensen, Bernard, D.C. *Empty Harvest: Understanding the Link Between Our Food, Our Immunity, and Our Planet*. Avery Publishing Group Inc.: Garden City Park, NY, 1990, p. 45, ©1990 Avery Publishing Group Inc. (800) 548-5757. Quotations reprinted by permission.
9. Mintz, Morton. *By Prescription Only*. 2nd ed. Houghton Mifflin, 1967, p. 130.
10. Levenstein, Harvey. *Paradox of Plenty: A Social History of Eating in Modern America*. Oxford University Press: New York, NY, 1993, p. 210, ©1993 Oxford University Press. All

rights reserved. Quotations reprinted by permission.

11. Zwerdling, Daniel, "The Food Monopolies," *Progressive*, Jan. 1975, p. 15.

12. Valentine, Tom, Valentine, Carole and Spounias, James. *Search for Health: A Classic Anthology*. Valentine Communications: Naples, FL, 1995, p. 135. Available from Carotec: (800)522-4279.

13. *Interlocking Directorates Among The Major U.S. Corporations*. June 15 (Legislative day May 17), 1978, U.S. Government Printing Office: Washington, D.C., 1978.

14. Levenstein, p. 171. [Levenstein's source: Senate Nutrition Committee. *Nutrition and Private Industry*. pp. 3888-4081.]

15. Stitt, Paul. *Beating the Food Giants*. Natural Press: Manitowoc, WI, 1993, p. 55.

16. Hitchcox, Lee, D.C. *Long Life Now*. Celestial Arts: Berkeley, CA, 1996, p. 19.

17. Stitt, p. 60.

Chapter 3: Unhealthy Consequences

1. *Cancer Statistics: 1996*. A Cancer Journal for Clinicians. American Cancer Society, Inc., Jan./Feb., Vol. 46, No. 1, 1996.

2. National Center for Health Statistics, Advance Report of Final Mortality Statistics, 1993.

3. Jensen, p. 126.

4. Mullins, Eustace. *Murder By Injection*. The National Council for Medical Research: Staunton, VA, 1995, p. 59.

5. American Cancer Society. "Cancer in Children." *Cancer Facts and Figures*. 1993, p. 14.

6. Miller, Bruce. *Antioxidants Made Simple*. Bruce Miller Enterprises Inc.: Dallas, TX, 1995, p. 17.

7. Flanagan, Patrick and Flanagan, Gail. *Elixir of the Ageless*. 2nd ed. Vortex Press: Flagstaff, AZ, 1996.

8. U.S. Department of Health and Human Services, *The Surgeon's Report on Nutrition and Health*, 1988.

9. "Self-reported Frequent Mental Distress Among Adults—United States, 1993-1996." *JAMA*. No. 22, June 10, 1998: 1772(2). [Cited in Simontacchi, p. 24, as per note 11].

10. Brown, Anne. "Mood Disorders in Children and Adolescents." *NARSAD Research Newsletter*, Winter 1996. [Cited in Simontacchi, p. 24, as per note 11].

11. Simontacchi, Carol. *The Crazy Makers: How The Food Industry Is Destroying Our Brains And Harming Our Children*. Jeremy Tarcher/Putnam: New York, NY, 2000, pp.25-26.

12. Glazer, Martha. "Annual Rx Survey," *Drug Topics*. April 8, 1996, p. 97. [Cited in Simontacchi, p. 26]

Chapter 4: Processed Foods

1. Jensen, p. 126.

2. *U.S. News & World Report*. Dec. 7, 1959. [Cited in Levenstein, p. 109]

3. Stitt, pp. 52, 137.

4. Deneen, Sally. "Body of Evidence: Were Humans Meant to Eat Meat?" www.emagazine.com. Jan-Feb, 2002.

5. Gerber, Michael, M.D. "Infant Soy Formula: A Safe Replacement of Mother's Milk?" *Alternative Medicine*. Issue 41, May 2000, pp. 104-106.

6. Stitt, p. 180.

7. "Breakfast Cereals," *Consumer Reports*, May 1961, p. 238.

8. Stitt, pp. 40-43.

9. Ibid., p. 42.

10. Senate Consumer Subcommittee. *Nutritional Content and Advertising.* p. 87. [Cited in Levenstein, p. 192.]

11. Stitt, p. 53.

12. Enig, Mary, Ph. D. "Trans fatty acids: An update." *Nutrition Quarterly*, 1993, 17(4): 79-95.

13. Bernstein, J., et al. "Depression of Lymphocyte Transformation Following Glucose Ingestion." *Am. J. Clin. Nutr.*, 30:613, 1977.

14. Hitchcox, p. 86.

15. Mullins, p. 125.

16. Bergner, Paul. *The Healing Power of Minerals.* Prima Publishing: Rocklin, CA, 1997, p. 209.

17. Ibid., p. 254.

18. Blaylock, Russel, M.D. *Excitotoxins: The Taste that Kills.* Heath Press: Santa Fe, New Mexico, 1997, p. 217.

19. Roberts, H.J., M.D. "Aspartame (NutraSweet®) Addiction." *Townsend Letter for Doctors and Patients.* Jan. 2000, #198, pp. 52-57.

20. DeLangre, Jacques, Ph. D. *Seasalt's Hidden Powers.* Happiness Press: Magalia, CA, 1994.

21. Scheuplein, Robert, Ph. D. Office of Toxicological Services, Center for Food Safety. Food and Drug Administration. Feb. 19, 1990. [Cited in Winter, 1991, p. 5.]

22. Jensen, p. 127.

23. Stitt, p. 120.

24. Ibid., p. 211.

25. Winter, Ruth, M.S. *A Consumer's Dictionary of Food Additives.* 4th ed., Random House, Inc.: New York, NY, 1994, p. 416.

26. Bergner, p. 36.

27. "Present-day Feeding Practice Report." U.S. Department of Public Health. Nov. 9, 1974. [Cited in Hitchcox, p. 17.]

28. Mindell, Earl, R. Ph., Ph. D. *Earl Mindell's Safe Eating.* Warner Books, Inc.: New York, NY, 1997, p.79.

29. Hunter, Beatrice Trum. *Additives Book.* Keats Publishing: New Canaan, CT, 1980, p. 77.

30. Hitchcox, p. 60.

31. Mindell, p. 124.

32. Blaylock, pp. 248-252.

33. Winter, 1994, p. 384.

34. Hitchcox, p. 66.

35. U.S. National Association of Pizza Operators. 1990.

36. Tribole, E. *Eating on the Run.* 2nd ed. Leisure Press, 1992, p. 1.

37. U.S. Bureau of the Census, Statistical Abstract of the United States: 1972., 112th ed., U.S. Government Printing Office, 1992, p. 134. [Source: Hitchcox, p. 86.]

Chapter 5: Additives

1. Winter, 1991, p. 5.

2. Winter, 1994, p. 7.

3. Ibid., p. 9.

4. Ibid.

5. *The Washington Post.* Jan. 23, 1988.

6. Efron, E. *The Apocalyptics.* Touchstone, 1984, p. 97. [Cited in Hitchcox, p. 290.]

7. Winter, 1994, p. 10.

8. Selikoff, Irving, M.D. "Second Sunday." NBC Television. Mar. 9, 1969.

9. Jensen, p. 61.

10. Grussendorf, O.W. "Removing Pesticide Residues from Food." *Biodynamics*, No. 76, Fall 1965, pp. 28-29.

11. Jensen, p. 58.

12. Regenstein, L. *How to Survive in America the Poisoned.* Acropolis Books, 1982, p. 103.

13. National Research Council. *Toxicity Testing: Strategies to Determine Needs and Priorities*. National Academy Press: Washington, D.C., 1994. [Cited in Winter, 1994, p. 1.]

14. Robbins, as per note 18, p. 318.

15. *The New York Times*. October 29, 1968. [Cited in Levenstein, p. 161.]

16. U.S. GAO. "Better Regulation of Pesticide Exports and Pesticide Residues in Imported Foods Is Essential." Report No. CED-79-43, June 22, 1979, p. 39.

17. "Environmental Quality—1975," The Sixth Annual Report of the Council on Environmental Quality, Washington, D.C., Dec. 1975, p. 369. [Cited in Robbins, as per note 18, p. 319.]

18. Robbins, John. *Diet for a New America*. ©1987, pp. 319-320. Copyright © 1987. Quotations re-printed by permission of H J Kramer/New World Library, Novato, CA. www.newworld-library.com. Toll-free 800/972-6657 ext. 52.

19. Robbins, pp. 322-323. [Robbins' source: "The EPA and the Regulation of Pesticides," Staff Report to the Subcommittee on Administrative Practice and Procedure, U.S. Senate, December 1976, p. 24.]

20. Scheehter, A. "Dioxins in Humans and the Environment. Biological Basis for Risk Assessment of Dioxins and Related Compounds." *Banbury Report*. 35:169, 1991. [Cited in Hitchcox, p. 220.]

21. Robbins, p. 321. [Robbins' source: Courtney, D., Dr. Testimony before Senate Commerce Committee Subcommittee on the Environment, August 9, 1974.]

22. Nordland, R. and Freedman, J. "Poison at Our Doorstep." *Philadelphia Enquirer*. Reprint. September 23-28, 1979.

23. "Environmental Quality—1979," *The Tenth Annual Report of the Council on Environmental Quality*. Washington, D.C., Dec. 1979. [Cited in Robbins, p. 321]

24. Regenstein, L. *How to Survive in America the Poisoned*. Acropolis Books: 1982, p. 103.

25. Robbins, p. 321.

26. Ibid., p. 348.

27. Ibid., pp. 315-316.

28. Ibid., p. 333.

29. Ibid.

30. Robbins, p. 333. [Robbins' source: Grzech, E. and Warbelow, K. "Distribution Hid Facts of PBB Peril." *Detroit Free Press*. March 13-15, 1977.]

31. Jensen, p. 69.

32. Hitchcox, pp. 46-52.

33. Winter, 1991.

34. "Effects, Uses, Control and Research of Agricultural Pesticides," *A Report by the Survey's and Investigations Staff, USDA*, 1966, Part I, p. 174. [Cited in Robbins, p. 337.]

35. Winter, 1991, p. 3.

36. Zaven, M.R., et al. "Chlorinated Hydrocarbons Insecticide Content of the Neonate," *Annals of the New York Academy of Sciences*, 160 (June 23, 1969): pp. 196-200. [Cited in Winter, 1991, p. 7.]

37. Environmental Working Group (EWG), Press Release of Jan. 29, 1998.

38. Harris, S. "Organochlorine Contamination of Breast Milk," Environmental Defense Fund. Washington, D.C., Nov. 7, 1979. [Cited in Robbins, p. 315.]

39. Jensen, p. 61.

40. Feichtinger, W. "Environmental Factors and Fertility." *Human Reprod.* 6:1170, 1991.

41. Heifetz, R. "Mother's Milk or Mother's Poison? Pesticides in Breast Milk." *J. Pest. Reform.* 9:15, 1989.

42. Hitchcox, p. 240.

43. As per note 75.

44. USDA Agricultural Marketing Service. "Pesticide Data Program: Summary of 1992 Data." April, 1994.

45. EPA Study. "Unfinished Business: A Comparative Assessment of Environmental Problems." Feb. 1987. [Cited in Hitchcox, p. 222.]

46. Lowe, C. *Toxic Food.* Avon Books. 1990, p. 8.

47. Gibbons, Boyd. "Do We Treat Our Soil Like Dirt?" *National Geographic.* Vol. 166, No. 3, Sept. 1984, pp. 350-351. ©1984 National Geographic Society. All rights reserved.

48. Trace Mineral Research; promotional brochure.

49. United States Senate, 74th Congress, 2nd Session, Document No. 264, United States Government Printing Office, Washington, D.C., June 1, 1936.

50. Mullins, p. 191.

51. Wilson, Duff. "Fear in the Fields." *The Seattle Times.* July 3, 1997, pp. 1-2, ©1997 Seattle Times Company. All rights reserved. Quotations reprinted by permission.

52. Ibid., p. 1.

53. Ibid., pp. 4-5.

54. Ibid., p. 4.

55. Ibid., p. 5.

56. Ibid., p. 4.

57. Winter, 1991, p. 103.

58. Robbins, p. 312

59. Ibid., p. 313.

60. Shell, O. *Modern Meats.* Vintage Books, Random House, 1985, pp. 283-284.

61. Winter, 1991, p. 102.

62. Hulse, p. 239.

63. Ibid., p. 232.

64. Ibid., p. 231.

65. "Shame on Them." *Food & Water.* Fall 1994, p. 2.

66. Hulse, p. 238.

67. Ibid.

68. Levy, Stuart, M.D. "The Challenge of Antibiotic Resistance." *Scientific American.* March, 1998, p. 51.

69. "Food Additive Status List Updated Jan. 1, 1988." Inspection Operations Manual Transmittal Notice, FDA. [Cited in Winter, 1991, p. 93.]

70. Levy, 1998, p. 51.

71. Begley, Sharon. "The End of Antibiotics." *Newsweek.* March 28, 1994, Newsweek, Inc. All rights reserved. Quotations reprinted by permission, p. 48.

72. Ibid.

73. Levy, Stuart, M.D. *The Antibiotic Paradox: How Miracle Drugs Are Destroying the Miracle.* Plenum Press: New York, N.Y., 1992.

74. Begley, p. 47.

75. ABC Radio News, May, 1998.

76. Begley, p. 49.

77. Ibid.

78. Levy, 1998, p. 46, ©1998 *Scientific American.* All rights reserved. Quotation reprinted by permission.

79. Nuland, Sherwin, M.D. *How We Die: Reflections on Life's Final Chapter.* Vintage Books: New York, NY, 1993.

80. *JAMA.* 275:189-93, 1996.

81. Levy, 1998, p. 51.

82. Begley, p. 48.

83. Ibid.

84. Ibid., pp. 48-49.

85. Winter, 1991, p. 96.

86. Hulse, p. 218.

Chapter 6: Food-borne Pathogens
1. Hulse, p. 212.
2. Ibid., p. 215.
3. Ibid., p. 210.
4. *National Geographic*. Feb. 1970. [Cited in Robbins, p. 63.]
5. Robbins, p. 66. [Robbins' source: Mason, J. and Singer, P. *Animal Factories*. Crown Publishers, 1980]
6. Robbins, p. 67. [Robbins' source: Shurter, D. et al. "The Meat You Eat." *The Plain Truth*. Oct.-Nov., 1970.]
7. Bronstein, Scott. "Chicken: How Safe?," *The Atlanta Journal-Constitution*. Reprint of Sunday, May 26, 1991, p. C1.
8. Ibid.
9. Ibid., p. C2.
10. Johnson, E. *Cancer Detection and Prevention*. Vol. 18(1)09-30, 1994.
11. Robbins, pp. 81-82. [Robbins' source: Brynes, J. "Raising Pigs by the Calendar at Maplewood Farms." *Hog Farm Management*. Sept. 1996, p. 30.]
12. Robbins, p. 85. [Robbins' source: Taylor, L. *National Hog Farmer*. March 1978, p. 27.]
13. Smith, R. *Farm Journal*. Dec. 1973. [Cited in Robbins, p. 109.]
14. Robbins, p. 110.
15. Fox, Nicols. *Spoiled: The Dangerous Truth About a Food Chain Gone Haywire*. BasicBooks: New York, NY, 1997, p. 249, ©1997 Harper Collins. All rights reserved. Quotations reprinted by permission.
16. Ibid., p. 250.
17. Ibid., p. 262.
18. Marsden, James L. Issues Briefing: "Issue: *E. coli* 0157:H7," American Meat Institute. July 1992. [Cited in Fox, p. 410.]

19. Hulse, p. 256.
20. Fox, p. 256.
21. Howard, Thomas. "Is Bovine Leukemia Out of Control?," *Hoards Dairyman*. Aug.25, 1992, p. 571. [Cited in Hulse, p. 149.]
22. Hulse, p. 150.
23. Ibid., p. 151.
24. Hehlmann, R. "RNA Tumor Viruses and Human Cancer." Current Topics in Microbiology and Immunology. 73:141-215, 1976. [Cited in Hulse, p. 154.]
25. Ferrer, J.F., M.D. Bovine Lymphosarcoma. The Compendium on Continuing Education for the Practicing Veterinarian. Vol. ii, No. II, pp. 235-242, 1980. [Cited in Hulse, p. 156.]
26. Hulse, p. 159.
27. *Lancet*. Nov. 27, 1976, pp. 1184-1186.
28. Hitchcox, pp. 42-43.
29. Liebman, B. "Lessons from China." CSPI Nutrition Action Healthletter, Dec. 1990, p. 6. [Cited in Hitchcox, p. 43]
30. Gonda, M.A., et al. "Bovine Immunodeficiency Virus: Molecular Biology and Virus-Host Interaction." Virus Research. 32:155-181, 1994. [Cited in Hulse, p. 187.]
31. Hulse, pp. 187, 193.
32. Ibid., p. 186.
33. Ibid.
34. Ibid., p. 192.
35. Hadlow, William, DVM. "An Overview of Scrapie in the United States," *JAMA*. Vol. 196, No. 10, May 15, 1990, p. 1676.
36. Hulse, p. 36.
37. Fox, p. 294.
38. Mathews, D. "Bovine Spongiform Encephalopathy." *J. Roy. Soc. Health*. Feb. 1991, pp. 3-5.

39. Brown, P., et al. "Resistance of Scrapie Infectivity to Steam Autoclaving after Formaldehyde Fixation and Limited Survival after Ashing at 360 degrees C: Practical and Theoretical Implications." *Journal of Infectious Diseases*, 1990, pp. 161, 467-472.

40. Hulse, p. 18.

41. Fox, p. 303. [Fox's source: Zane, Peder, J. "It Ain't for Meat; It's for Lotion," *The New York Times*. May 5, 1996.]

42. Carrel, Chris. "Mad Cows Ate My Brain." *Seattle Weekly*. March 12, 1998, p. 27.

43. Rampton, Sheldon and Stauber, John. *Mad Cow U.S.A.* Common Courage Press: Monroe, ME, 1997.

44. Blakeslee, Sandra. "Disease Fear Prompts New Look at Rendering." *The New York Times*, March 11, 1997.

45. Fox, p. 304.

46. Hulse, p. 21.

47. Deley, Suzanne. "Mad Cow Disease Panicing Europe as Incidents Rise." *The New York Times*, Dec. 1, 2000, p. A1.

48. Hulse, p. 28.

49. Ibid., p. 30.

50. "BSE Experts Give Up Beef," *Agscene*. No. 102, Spring, 1991.

51. Hulse, p. 30.

52. Ibid., p. 134.

53. Hueston, William, et al. "Bovine Spongiform Encepholopathy," *Animal Health Insight*, Fall, 1992, pp. 1-7.

54. Fox, p. 295.

55. Hulse, p. 16.

56. Ibid., p. 60.

57. Carrel, p. 27.

58. Hulse, p. 105.

59. Fox, p. 307.

60. *Food Chemical News*, June 3, 1996.

61. Fox, p. 312. [Fox's source: McNair, Joel. "Experts Argue Over BSE Measures," *Agri-views*, Sept. 16, 1993.]

62. Ibid., p. 311.

63. Ibid., p. 312.

64. Marsh, R.F., et al. Epidemiology and Experimental Studies on a New Incident of Transmissible Mink Encephelopathy," *Journal of General Virology*, 1991, pp. 72, 589-594.

65. Meilke, James. "Millions at Risk from CJD," *The Guardian*, Sat. Jan. 8, 2000.

66. Hulse, p. 26.

67. Ibid., p. 19.

68. Ibid., p. 28.

69. Ibid.

70. The Observer. Oct. 22, 2000; www.newsunlimited.co.uk; [Cited in *Nexus*. "Vaccines Contaminated with Mad Cow Disease?" Jan.-Feb. 2001, p. 9]; www.nexusmagazine.com

71. "Mad Cow Disease and Makeup, New Fears." CBC, Toronto, Tues., Jan. 23, 2001.

72. Mullins, p. 140-142.

73. *Lancet*. July 7, 1990.

74. Boller, Francis, et al. "Diagnosis of Dementia: Clinicalopathologic Correlations." *Neurology*. Jan.: 39(1):769, 1989.

75. Hulse, p. 114.

76. Ibid., p. 60.

77. Carrel, pp. 30-32.

78. Ibid., p. 32.

79. Winter, 1991, pp. 135-136.

80. Ibid., p. 122.

81. Regenstein, p. 298.

82. Hitchcox, pp. 70-71

83. Winter, 1991, pp. 139-140.

84. Robbins, p. 331.

85. Barker, Rodney. *And the Waters Turned to Blood*. Simon & Schuster: New York, NY, 1997.

86. Lederberg, Joshua, M.D. and Shope, Robert, M.D. *Emerging Infec-*

tions: *Microbial Threats to Health in the United States*. Institute of Medicine: Washington, D.C., 1992.
87. Motavalli, Jim. "The Case Against Meat." www.emagazine.com. Jan.-Feb., 2002.

Chapter 7: Other Contaminants
1. Jensen, p. 46.
2. Hitchcox, Lee, D.C. "Secret Changes Threaten Our Food Supply," *Health Freedom News*. Sept.-Oct., 1996, p. 59.
3. Ibid.
4. Walker, Morton, M.D. "Genetic Manipulations Create New Frankenstein Foods." *Search For Health*, May/June, 1993, pp. 38-40.
5. Ribeiro, Silvia. www.etcgroup.org.
6. Mullins, p. 223.
7. Winter, 1991, p. 241.
8. Mullins, p. 225.
9. Ziporin, Z., et al. "Vitamin Content of Foods Exposed to Ionizing Radiation." *Journal of Nutrition*. Vol. 63, No. 2, Oct. 10, 1957, pp. 201-209.
10. Jensen, p. 18.
11. Mullins, p. 225.
12. Fitch, Ed. "Scouts Agree: It's Hot If It's Microwavable." *Advertising Age*. May 9, 1988, S16. [Cited in Winter, 1991, p. 237.]
13. Valentine, pp. 8-22.
14. Ibid., p. 10.
15. Ibid., p. 11
16. Ibid., pp. 19-21.
17. Ibid., p. 14.

Chapter 8: Water
1. Interim Report on Ground Water Contamination, House Committee on Government Operations, Sept. 30, 1980. [Cited in Winter, 1991, p. 181.]
2. A'o, Lono Kahuna Kupua. *Don't*

Drink the Water. Kali Press: Pagosa Springs, CO, 1998, p. 9.
3. Orr, Scott. "Jersey Ranks No. 20 on Toxic Pollutants List." *Newark Star-Ledger*. June 20, 1989, p. 6. [Cited in Winter, 1991, p. 182.]
4. Winter, 1991, p. 184.
5. von Radowitz, John. *PA News*, Sunday, Jan. 9, 2000
6. A'o, p. 27.
7. *The New York Times*, June 2, 1995.
8. Mullins, p. 189.
9. Winter, 1991, p. 190.
10. *Acres, USA*. April, 1989. [Source: Jensen, pp. 132-133.]
11. A'o, pp. 45-47.
12. Donsbach, Kurt, D.C., Ph.D. *Water*. Wholistic Publications: Baja, Mexico, 1989, p. 41.
13. Mullins, p. 148.
14. Ibid.
15. Jensen, p. 136.
16. A'o, p. 49.
17. *Newsweek*. Feb. 5, 1990. [Source: A'o, p. 49.]
18. Hitchcox, p. 234.
19. Jensen, p. 129.
20. Ibid.
21. Mindell, p. 24.
22. Ibid., p. 25.
23. Ibid., p. 22.
24. Bryce, Susan. "HydroDollars: The Privatization of Water." *Nexus*, May-June, 2001, p. 25.

Chapter 9: The Alternatives
1. Price, Weston, DDS. *Nutrition and Physical Degeneration*. 6th ed. Keats Publishing: New Canaan, CT, 1997.
2. Hitchcox, p. 102.
3. Hindhede, M. "The Effect of Food Restriction During War on Mortality in Copenhagen." *JAMA*. 74:381, 1920. [Cited in Hitchcox, p. 81.]

4. Ingram, D. "Trends in Diet and Breast Cancer Mortality in England and Wales, 1928-1977." *Nutr. and Cancer.* 3:75, 1982. [Cited in Hitchcox, p. 81.]

5. Hitchcox, p. 64.

6. Robbins, p. 345.

7. Smith, B. "Organic Foods vs. Supermarket Foods: Element Levels." *Journal of Applied Nutrition,* 45(1), 1993, pp. 35-38.

8. Pimentel, D. "Environmental and Economic Costs of Pesticide Use." *BioScience.* 42:750, 1992.

9. Hitchcox, p. 71.

10. Linde, et al. "St. John's Wort for Depression: An Overview and Meta-Analysis of Randomized Clinical Trials." *The British Medical Journal.* 313(7052): 253, 1996.

Chapter 10: Supper Supplements

1. Shamsuddin, A.M., M.D., Ph. D. *IP$_6$: Nature's Revolutionary Cancer-Fighter.* Kensington Books: New York, NY, 1998.

   Coles, L.S., M.D., Ph. D. and Steinman, David. *The IP$_6$ with Inositol Question and Answer Book.* Freedom Press: Topanga, CA, 1999.

2. Ber, Leonid, M.D., and Gazella, Karolyn. *Activate Your Immune System.* IMPAKT Communication, Inc.: Green Bay, WI, 1998.

3. Sharamon, Shalila and Baginski, Bodo. *The Healing Power of Grapefruit Seed.* Lotus Light Publications: Twin Lakes, WI, 1995.

4. Walker, Morton, M.D. *Olive Leaf Extract.* Kensington Books: New York, NY, 1997.

5. Ingram, Cass, D.O. *The Cure is in The Cupboard: How to Use Oregano for Better Health.* Knowledge House: Buffalo Grove, Il, 1997.

INDEX